16

Pilgrim's Progress

Simplified

Based on
John Bunyan's *allegory*

D1166093

A Beka Book®
A MINISTRY OF
PENSACOLA CHRISTIAN COLLEGE
PENSACOLA, FLORIDA 32523-9160

Marion Hedquist—edition editor

Michelle Johnson—designer

Illustrators—Brian Jekel, Kyle Henry, Scott Lyle, Mike Davis

Third Edition

Copyright © 1997, 1986, 1975 Pensacola Christian College
All rights reserved. Printed in U.S.A. 2005 C97

A Beka Book, a Christian textbook ministry affiliated with Pensacola Christian College, is designed to meet the need for Christian textbooks and teaching aids. The purpose of this publications ministry is to help Christian schools reach children and young people for the Lord and train them in the Christian way of life.

Background on edge of pages and with headings courtesy Corel Corporation.

John Bunyan
1628–1688

John Bunyan

Introduction

A Brave Man's Dream

Sometimes when we have problems, we become angry and want to give up. John Bunyan, who wrote *Pilgrim's Progress,* had more problems than we can imagine, yet he did not become angry or discouraged. Instead, in the middle of all his problems, he wrote one of the greatest books in all history. That book is *Pilgrim's Progress*.

John Bunyan was born over three hundred years ago in England. At that time most Englishmen were very poor. John's parents saved every extra penny to send him to school. At school Bunyan fell in with some wicked playmates. He picked up many of their evil ways. Since he did not go to church, he had not been taught that what he was doing was wrong. As Bunyan grew older, he sank deeper and deeper into sin. Finally, he overheard some women talking about the Bible. He became interested in the Bible and started reading it every night. He learned from the Bible that Jesus died for our sins and that only He can take away our sins. With joyful heart, John Bunyan accepted Jesus Christ as Savior.

Bunyan began preaching right away. Most of the churches in England at that time did not teach the whole truth of the Bible. They did not like Bunyan's preaching, because he told people that they needed to be saved. When the people started leaving their old churches to hear John Bunyan, the churches told Bunyan to stop preaching.

Bunyan, of course, did not stop preaching. He knew that he could not stop for he wanted to please God rather than men. Because he did what was right, Bunyan was thrown into prison.

Now, prisons in the 1600s were very different from modern-day prisons. There were no beds, just hard wooden benches. There were no lights, just a small window to let in a little sunshine. No nice warm heaters for Bunyan; the cell was cold and damp. It was a horrible place.

Was Bunyan discouraged? No! He kept singing, praying, and reading the Bible. That was the source of his strength. After a few months he became sick, but he did not give up hope. He was going to stay true to God no matter what. How strong Bunyan's faith was!

Bunyan's main problem in prison was finding something to do. After a wonderful dream one night, Bunyan began writing the story of a man who came to know Christ just as he had. Bunyan made the Christian life sound like a journey on a straight and narrow road. For many weeks he worked on the book. When he was let out of jail, he took the book to a printer to be published. He named the book *Pilgrim's Progress*.

As you read *Pilgrim's Progress,* watch for problems that Christian faced that Bunyan himself may have faced in his lifetime. Although it is not a true story, *Pilgrim's Progress* takes facts from the Bible and explains the way to be saved by trusting in Christ. Most books written in Bunyan's time have been thrown away and forgotten, but three hundred years after it was written, *Pilgrim's Progress* is still famous. It is truly a living tribute to a man who proved that faith in God will always be rewarded, if not in this life, then in the bright Celestial City that lies at the end of every Christian pilgrim's journey.

The Pilgrim's Journey

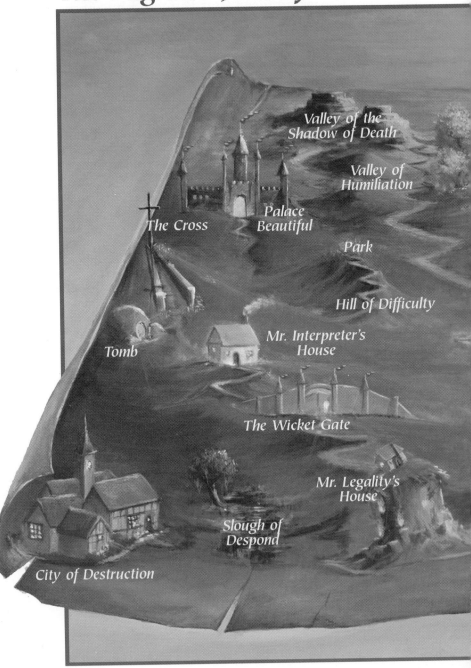

Valley of the
Shadow of Death

Valley of
Humiliation

The Cross

Palace
Beautiful

Park

Hill of Difficulty

Tomb

Mr. Interpreter's
House

The Wicket Gate

Mr. Legality's
House

Slough of
Despond

City of Destruction

Chapter 1

As I went through the wild waste of this world, I came to a place where there was a den, and I lay down in it to sleep. While I slept, I had a dream, and lo! I saw a man who was dressed in rags. He stood with his face turned away from his own house. He had a Book in his hand and a great burden on his back. I saw him read from the pages of a Book, and as he read, he wept and shook with fear. Then he broke out with a loud cry, and said, "What shall I do to be saved?"

In this condition he went home, and as long as he could, he kept quiet. He did not want his wife and children to see how troubled he was. But finally he told them what was on his mind. "Oh, my dear wife, and you my children," he said, "I am full of woe, for I am

---

burden—a heavy load
condition—state of mind; state of health
woe—a condition of deep suffering or grief
soothe—to make calm; to ease
harsh—rude; rough; unpleasantly sharp

ignore—to pay no attention to
evangelist—a traveling preacher
wrath—great anger
wicket gate—a small gate set near a larger one

carrying a heavy burden. And more than this, I have been told that our town will be destroyed with fire, in which all of us shall be lost if no way is found to save us."

"Friends"

All who heard this sad tale were amazed, not because they thought that what the man said was true, but because they had fears that something was wrong with his mind. They said that sleep might soothe his brain, and with all haste they got him to bed.

When the morning broke, they asked him how he did. He told them, "Worse and worse," and he started talking once more the way he had before, but they would not listen. By and by, to drive off his fit, they spoke harsh words to him. At times they would laugh, at times they would scold, and sometimes they would ignore him. So he went to his room to pray for them, as well as to think over his problem. He would go, too, into the woods to read and think, and thus for some weeks he spent his time.

Evangelist

Now I saw, in my dream, that one day while he was walking in the fields with his Book in his hand, he gave a groan. He felt as if a cloud were on his soul, and he burst out again and said, "Who will save me?" I saw, too, that he gave wild looks this way and that, as if he wanted to run away. Yet he stood still, for he could not tell which way to go. At last, a man whose name was Evangelist came up to him and said, "Why dost thou weep?"

Fear

He said, "Sir, I see by this Book in my hand that I am to die, and that then God will judge me. Sir, I am afraid to die."

Evangelist: "Why do you fear to die, since this life is so full of sadness?"

The man said, "I am afraid that I shall be punished, and that this burden on my back will make me sink down into the Lake of Fire."

"If this be your case," said Evangelist, "why do you stand still?"

But the man said, "I know not where to go."

The Scroll

Then Evangelist gave him a scroll with these words on it, "Flee from the wrath to come." When the man read it he said, "Which way must I flee?"

Evangelist held out his hand to point to a gate in a wide field and said, "Do you see the Wicket Gate?"

The man said, "No."

"Do you see that light?"

He then said, "I think I do."

"Keep that light in your eye," said Evangelist, "and go straight up to it. Then you shall see the gate. Knock at this gate and it shall be told you what you are to do."

Then I saw in my dream that Christian— for that was his name— began to run.

Thinking It Through

1. What was Christian's burden?

2. How did he know about his burden?

3. What question did Christian ask? What is the answer to Christian's question?

4. What man helped Christian? What did he tell Christian?

Acts 16:30, 31

"And brought them out, and said, Sirs, what must I do to be saved?

"And they said, Believe on the Lord Jesus Christ, and thou shalt be saved, and thy house."

Chapter 2

hristian had not gone far from his own door, when his wife and young ones gave a loud wail to beg him to come back. But the man put his hands to his ears and ran on with a cry of "Life! Life!"

The friends of his wife, too, came out to see him run; and as he went, some made fun of him and some threatened him. Two men, Obstinate and Pliable, tried to carry him back by force. Now, these two men were like their names, for "Obstinate" means *stubborn,* and "Pliable" means *easy to bend.* By this time, Christian was far from the town, but at last Obstinate and Pliable caught up to him.

Then Christian said, "Friends, why are you come?"

"To bid you go back with us," said they.

---

obstinate (äb′stə·nĭt)—stubborn
pliable (plī′ə·b'l)—easy to bend
wail—a long, pitiful cry of grief or pain
bid—to command, ask, or tell
destruction—the state of being
    destroyed

spare—extra
bliss—great joy or
    happiness
nay—no

Good Advice

But," Christian said, "that can not be. You dwell in the City of Destruction, the place where I, too, was born. I know it to be so, and there you will die and sink down to a place which burns with fire. Be wise, good friends, and come with me."

"What! and leave all the things we own, and our friends and families?"

"Yes," said Christian, "for all which you might leave is but a grain compared to that which I seek. If you will go with me and stand firm, you shall do as well as I. Where I go, you will find all you want and to spare. Come with me, and see if my words are true."

Stubborn Obstinate

Obstinate: "What are the things that you seek, since you leave all the world to find them?"

Christian: "I seek those joys that fade not, which are laid up in a place of bliss—safe there for those who go in search of them. Read it so, if you will, in my Book."

Obstinate: "Tush! Off with your Book. Will you go back with us or no?"

Christian: "No, not I, for I have laid my hand to the plow."

Obstinate: "Come, friend Pliable, let us turn back and leave such a fool. People like him get a crazy idea and end up more wise in their own eyes than ten men who know how to think."

Pliable's Choice

Pliable: "Nay, do not scorn him. If what the good Christian says is true, he has more sense than we do. My heart tells me to go with this man."

Obstinate: "What! Will you be a fool, too? Go back, go back, and be wise."

Christian: "Nay, but come with your friend Pliable. There are such things to be had as those I just spoke of, and more too. If you will not listen to me, read here in this Book which comes to us from God, Who could not lie."

Pliable: "Well, friend Obstinate, I mean to go with this good man." Then said he to Christian, "Do you know the way to the place you speak of?"

Christian: "I am told by a man whose name is Evangelist to run for the gate that is in front of us. There I shall be told how to find the way."

Obstinate: "And I will go back to my home. I will not be one of you crazy people."

Thinking It Through

1. Why did Obstinate and Pliable come running after Christian?

2. What does "Obstinate" mean? What does "Pliable" mean?

3. Why did Christian refuse to go back with Obstinate and Pliable?

4. Who decided to go with Christian?

Matthew 7:13, 14

"Enter ye in at the straight gate: for wide is the gate, and broad is the way, that leadeth to destruction, and many there be which go in thereat:

"Because straight is the gate, and narrow is the way, which leadeth unto life, and few there be that find it."

Chapter 3

ow I saw in my dream, that Obstinate left, and Christian and Pliable set off to cross the plain, speaking together as they went.

Christian: "Well, Pliable, how do you do now? I am glad you decided to go with me."

Pliable: "Come, friend Christian, since just the two of us are here, tell me more about the things for which we are looking."

 Things To Come

Christian: "I can find them in my heart, though I know not how to speak of them with my tongue. But, since you wish to know, this Book tells us of an everlasting kingdom, and a life that has no end."

Pliable: "Well said; and what else?"

---

everlasting—never coming to an end; eternal
faith—a firm belief in God; belief in something not seen
slough (slou)—a place full of soft, deep mud
despond—to lose courage or hope

Christian: "That there are crowns of light to be given us, and robes that will make us shine like the sun."

Pliable: "This, too, is good; and what else?"

Christian: "That there shall be no more crying or sorrow; for He that owns the place will wipe all tears from our eyes."

Pliable: "And what friends shall we find there?"

Christian: "There we shall be with all the saints, in robes so bright that our eyes will grow dim to look on them. There shall we meet those who in this world have stood for the faith. We shall see those who have been burned at the stake and thrown to wild beasts because of their love for the Lord. They will not harm us, but will greet us with love, for they all walk in the sight of God."

The Way

Pliable: "But how shall we get to share all this?"

Christian: "We shall be shown the way when we reach the gate."

Pliable: "Well, my good friend, glad am I to hear of these things. Come on, let us go faster."

Christian: "I can not go as fast as I want to, because of this burden on my back."

The Slough of Despond

Then I saw in my dream that just as they had come to an end of this talk, they drew near to a swamp that was in the middle of the plain, and as they were not watching, they both fell in. The name of it was the Slough of Despond. Here they lay for a time in the mud, and the load that Christian had on his back made him sink all the more into the mud.

Pliable: "Ah! Friend Christian, where are you now?"

Christian: "In truth, I do not know."

Then Pliable said to his friend, "Is this the bliss of which you have told me all this while? If we have such a hard time when we first set out, what may we look for between this and the end of our way?"

And with that he got out of the mud on that side of the slough which was next to his own house. Off he went, and Christian saw him no more. So Pliable proved true to his name. It was easy to talk him into something that sounded good, but when trouble came he would turn back to his old ways. He did not really believe God at all.

Thinking It Through

1. What did Christian tell Pliable about the ever-lasting kingdom (Heaven)?

2. How can we make sure that we will go to Heaven?

3. What did Christian and Pliable fall into?

4. Why did Pliable turn back?

John 3:18

"He that believeth on Him is not condemned: but he that believeth not is condemned already, because he hath not believed in the name of the only begotten Son of God."

Chapter 4

hristian was left to tumble in the Slough of Despond as well as he could. Yet his aim was to reach the side of the slough that was near the Wicket Gate. At last he did this, but he could not get out because of the burden that was on his back. Then I saw in my dream that a man came to him whose name was Help.

"What do you do here?" said Help.

Christian: "I was told to go this way by Evangelist. He told me to pass up to yonder gate, that I might flee from the wrath to come. As I was going, I fell in here."

Help: "But why did you not look for the steps?"

Christian: "I was so afraid that I ran as fast as I could and fell in."

Help: "Give me your hand."

---

aim—purpose; goal; object
yonder—at a distance, but within sight
firm—solid; hard
bade—asked or told
scum—a thin layer of waste, impurity, or refuse

So he gave him his hand, and he drew him out, and set him on firm ground, and bade him go on his way.

 A Question

Then in my dream I went up to Help and said to him, "Sir, since this place is on the way from the City of Destruction to the Wicket Gate, how is it that no one repairs this patch of ground, so that those who come by may not fall into the slough?"

Help: "This slough is such a place as no one can repair. It is the spot to which doth run the scum and filth that come from sin. That is why men call it the Slough of Despond. When the man of sin wakes up to a sense of his own lost state, doubts and fears rise up in his soul, and all of them drain down and sink in this place. It is this that makes the ground so bad.

"True, there are good and sound steps in the midst of the slough, but at times it is hard to see them. Even when men do see them, their heads are so dull that they step to one side and fall into the mud. But the ground is good when they have once got in at the gate."

Pliable at Home

Now I saw in my dream that by this time Pliable had gone back to his house once more, and that his friends came to see him. Some called him a wise man for coming home, and some called him a fool for having started out in the first place. Others made fun of him, saying, "Well, had I set out, I would not have come back just because of a swamp in the road." So Pliable was left to sneak off, alone and ashamed.

Thinking It Through

1. Why could Christian not get out of the Slough of Despond alone?

2. What happened to Pliable when he returned home?

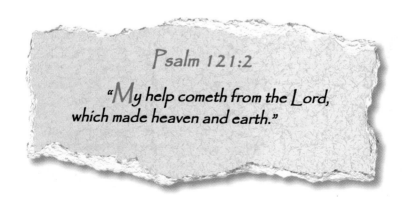

Psalm 121:2

"My help cometh from the Lord, which made heaven and earth."

Chapter 5

ow as Christian went on his way, he saw a man come through the field to meet him, whose name was Mr. Worldly Wiseman. He had heard some news of Christian, for his flight from the City of Destruction was now being talked about far and near. So he said, "How now, good sir, where do you go with such a burden on your back?"

Christian: "In truth, it is a burden; and if you ask me where I go, I must tell you, sir. I go to the Wicket Gate in front of me, for there I shall find a way to get rid of my burden."

Worldly Wiseman: "Have you not a wife and children?"

Christian: "Yes, but with this burden I do not seem to care for them as I did. In truth, I feel as if I had none."

---

worldly—loving only the pleasures of this world
urge—to plead with
aim—(noun) purpose; goal; object (verb) to point; to direct
risk—a chance of meeting danger or peril

ease—comfort; freedom from pain
morality—the holding of moral beliefs and high standards
legality—the belief that obeying the law will get one to Heaven
rank—social position

Worldly Wiseman: "Will you hear me if I speak my mind to you?"

Christian: "If what you say be good, I will, for I am much in need of help."

Much Talk

Worldly Wiseman: "I would urge you then, with all speed, to get rid of your burden; for your mind will not be at rest till then."

Christian: "That is just what I seek to do. But there is no man in our land who can take it from me."

Worldly Wiseman: "Who told you to go this way to be rid of it?"

Christian: "One that I took to be a great and true man; his name is Evangelist."

Worldly Wiseman: "Listen to what I say. There is no worse way in the world than that which he has sent you. You will find that out if you take him for your guide. In this short time you have already met with bad luck, for I see that the mud of the Slough of Despond is on your coat. Hear me, for I have seen more of the world than you. In the way you go, you will meet with pain, hunger, thirst, the sword, and even death! Take no heed of what Evangelist tells you."

Christian: "Why, sir, this burden on my back is worse to me than all those things of which you speak. I care not what I meet with in the way, if I can but get rid of my burden."

Worldly Wiseman: "How did you get it in the first place?"

Christian: "Why, I read this Book."

Worldly Wiseman: "Like other weak men that I know, who aim at things too high for them, you have lost heart. You run in the dark at great risk to gain you know not what."

Christian: "I know what I would gain. I want to get rid of my burden."

Worldly Wiseman: "But why will you seek for ease in this way, when I could show you a way to gain it without any risk?"

Christian: "Pray, sir, tell me what that way is."

Bad Advice

Worldly Wiseman: "Well, in yonder town, which you can see from here—the name of which is Morality—there dwells a man whose name is Legality. He is a wise man, and a man of some rank. He has ability to help men get rid of such burdens as yours. He will tell you that if you keep the Ten Commandments your burden will disappear.

"To him, as I said, you may go and get help. His house is but a mile from this place. There, I say, you may go to get rid of your burden. I would not have you go back to your old home, but you can send for your wife and children, and you will find that food there is cheap and good."

Christian thought for a moment, and then he said, "Sir, which is my way to this good man's house?"

Worldly Wiseman: "Do you see that hill?"

Christian: "Yes, I do."

Worldly Wiseman: "By that hill you must go, and the first house you come to is his."

Thinking It Through

1. What did Mr. Worldly Wiseman say would become of Christian if he followed the advice of Evangelist?

2. What was Worldly Wiseman's advice?

3. Was Worldly Wiseman's advice good?

4. What is the only way to be saved?

John 14:16

"And I will pray the Father, and He shall give you another Comforter, that He may abide with you for ever."

Chapter 6

So Christian went out of his way to find Mr. Legality's house to seek for help.

But, lo, when he had got close up to the hill, it was so steep and high that he was afraid it should fall on his head; so he stood still, not knowing what to do. His load, too, seemed to weigh more than when he was on the right road.

Then came flames of fire out of the hill, that made him quake for fear lest he should be burned. And now he was greatly grieved that he had listened to Worldly Wiseman.

---

quake—to shake or shudder
grieved—feeling grief or sorrow
blush—to become red in the face because of shame or embarrassment
dost—old English form of *do*

yield—to give up
heed—to pay close attention to; to take careful notice of
strive—to make great efforts; to try very hard
Godspeed—a farewell wish for safe travel

 ## Evangelist Returns

It was well that he just then saw Evangelist coming to meet him. At the sight of him, however, Christian felt a deep blush creep on his face for shame. Evangelist drew near, and when he came up to him, he said, with a sad look, "What dost thou here, Christian?"

To these words Christian knew not what to say, so he just stood. Then Evangelist went on: "Art not thou the man that I heard cry in the City of Destruction?"

Christian: "Yes, dear sir, I am the man."

Evangelist: "Did not I point out to thee the way to the Wicket Gate? Did I not tell you that there is only one way to get rid of your burden? You can not do it by keeping the Law, for you can never keep the whole Law."

Christian: "Yes, you told me all that, sir."

Evangelist: "How is it, then, that thou hast so soon gone out of the way?"

Christian: "When I had got out of the Slough of Despond I met a man who told me that in a town nearby, I might find one who could take off my burden."

Evangelist: "What was he?"

Christian: "He had fair looks, and said much to me, and got me at last to yield; so I came here. But when I saw this hill, and how steep it was, I stopped, lest it should fall on my head."

Evangelist: "What said the man to thee?"

 God's Word

When Evangelist had heard from Christian all that had taken place, he said: "Stand still a while, that I may show thee the words of God."

So Evangelist read, " 'Now the just shall live by faith, but if any man draw back, my soul shall have no pleasure in him.' Is not this the case with thee?" said he. "Hast not thou drawn back thy feet from the way of peace, to thine own cost? Dost thou not turn away from the most high God?"

Then Christian fell down at his feet as dead, and said, "Woe is me! Woe is me!"

At the sight of this, Evangelist caught him by the right hand and said, "All manner of sin shall be forgiven unto men. Be not faithless, but believing."

Then did Christian find some peace, and stood up.

A Scolding

Evangelist: "I pray thee give more heed to the things that I shall tell thee of. The Lord says, 'Strive to go in at the straight gate, the gate to which I send thee, for straight is the gate that leads to life, and few there be that find it.'

"Why didst thou take lightly the words of God, and listen to Mr. Worldly Wiseman? The Lord hath told thee that 'he who will save his life shall lose it.' He to whom thou wast sent for ease, Legality by name, could not set thee free. No man yet has got rid of his burden by trying to do right. He could only show thee the way to sorrow, for by the deeds of the Law no man can get rid of his burden. Mr. Worldly Wiseman and his friend Mr. Legality are false guides."

Now Christian, in great dread, could think of nothing but death, and was very sorry that he had left the right way. Then he spoke once more to Evangelist in these words: "Sir, what think you? Is there hope? May I now go back and try to reach the Wicket Gate? I grieve that I gave ear to this man's voice, but may my sin be forgiven?"

Evangelist: "Thy sin is great, for thou hast gone from the way that is good to walk in false paths. Yet the man at the gate will let thee through, for he has

love and good will for all men. But take heed that
thou turn not to the right hand nor to the left."

Then did Christian make a move to go back, and
Evangelist bade him Godspeed.

Thinking It Through

1. Why did Christian blush when he saw Evangelist?

2. Why can we not be saved by keeping the Law?

3. What good news did Evangelist give to Christian?

Titus 3:5

"Not by works of righteousness
which we have done, but according to
His mercy He saved us, by the washing
of regeneration, and renewing of the
Holy Ghost."

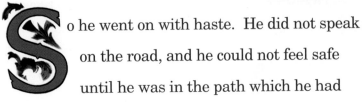

Chapter 7

So he went on with haste. He did not speak on the road, and he could not feel safe until he was in the path which he had left. In time he got up to the gate and read the sign over it: "Knock, and it shall be opened unto you." He gave two or three knocks and said, "May I enter in here?"

 Good-will

At last a man named Good-will came to the gate. "Who is there?" he called. "Where do you come from? What do you want?"

Christian: "I come from the City of Destruction with a load of sins on my back. I am on my way to Mount Zion, that I may be free from the wrath to

---

Zion (zī′ən)—a name often used for Heaven
flung—threw with force
Beelzebub (bē·ĕl′zə·bub′)—a name for Satan
reap—to harvest; to gather
worthwhile—being worth the time or effort spent

convince—to bring about belief; to prove
deliverance—a setting free; a rescue or release
interpreter—one who explains or tells the meaning of something

come. I have been told that my way is through this gate. I would know, sir, if you will let me in?"

Good-will: "With all my heart."

He flung back the gate. But just as Christian was stepping in, he gave him a pull.

Then said Christian, "What means that?"

Beelzebub's Fort

"A short way from this gate," said Good-will, "there is a strong fort. Beelzebub is the chief of that fort. He and his helpers shoot darts at all who come up to the gate to try to kill them before they get in."

Then said Christian, "I come in with joy and with fear." When he had entered, the man at the gate said, "Who sent you here?"

Christian: "Evangelist said I could come and knock. He said that you, sir, would tell me what I must do."

The Open Door

Good-will: "The door is thrown open wide for you to come in, and no man can shut it."

Christian: "Now I begin to reap the good of all the dangers I have met with on the way."

Good-will: "But how is it that no one comes with you?"

Christian: "None of my friends saw as I did that there was cause of fear."

 ## The Flight

Good-will: "Did they know of your flight?"

Christian: "Yes, my wife and young ones saw me go. I heard their cries as they ran out to try and stop me. Some of my friends tried to make me come home, but I put my hands to my ears, and so came on my way."

Good-will: "But did none of them come out to beg you to go back?"

Christian: "Yes, both Obstinate and Pliable came. But when they found that I would not yield, Obstinate went home, but Pliable came with me as far as the Slough of Despond."

Good-will: "Why did he not come through it?"

When Christian told him the rest, he said, "Ah, poor man! Is a world of joy such a small thing to him that he did not think it worthwhile to run a few risks to gain it?"

"Sir," said Christian, "there is not much difference between him and me."

Then he told Good-will how he had been led from the straight path by Mr. Worldly Wiseman.

Good-will: "Oh, did he get hold of you? What! He would try to convince you that you could be helped by Mr. Legality. They are, in truth, cheats. And did you listen to what he said?"

Christian's Joy

Christian then told him all. "But now that I am here," said he, "I am more fit for death than to stand and talk to my Lord. But oh, the joy it is to me to be here!"

Good-will: "We keep none out that knock at this gate, no matter what they have done before they came here; for they are 'in no wise cast out.' So, good Christian, come with me, and I will teach you the way you must go. Look before you. That is the way which was laid down by Christ and the wise men of old, and it is as straight as a ruler."

The Right Path

Christian: "But is there no turn or bend by which one who knows not the road might lose his way?"

Good-will: "My friend, there are many wide paths that lead down to it. Yet by this you may judge the right from the wrong—the right paths are straight and narrow."

Then I saw in my dream that Christian said, "Could you not help me off with this burden on my back?"

Good-will replied, "As to your burden, you must bear it until you come to the place of Deliverance, for there it will fall from your back."

Christian wanted to start off on the road right away, but Good-will said, "Stop awhile and let me tell you something. When you have gone through the gate, you will see the house of Mr. Interpreter. Knock at his door, and he will show you good things." Then Christian left his friend, who bade him Godspeed.

Thinking It Through

1. Who opened the gate for Christian?

2. Who is the chief of the strong fort near the gate?

3. Why do those in the fort shoot their darts?

4. Who can shut the gate?

5. What did Good-will do for Christian?

6. How is the right path different from the others?

Matthew 7:13, 14

"Enter ye in at the straight gate: for wide is the gate, and broad is the way, that leadeth to destruction, and many there be which go in thereat:

"Because straight is the gate, and narrow is the way, which leadeth unto life, and few there be that find it."

Chapter 8

Christian now went on until he came to the house of Mr. Interpreter. After he had knocked two or three times, someone came to the door and said, "Who is there?"

Christian: "I have come to see the good man of the house."

In a short time Mr. Interpreter himself came to him and said, "What would you have?"

Christian: "Sir, I am come from the City of Destruction, and I am on my way to Mount Zion. Mr. Good-will told me that if I came here you would show me good things that would help me."

---

grave—serious; solemn; sad
sole—the only one
grace—undeserved love or kindness
cleanse—to make clean
passion—strong desire
patience—the ability to bear pain or trials calmly

The Guide

Then Interpreter took Christian to a room and told his servant to bring a light. On the wall Christian saw the picture of One Who had a grave face. He was looking toward the sky, and the Best of Books was in His hand. The law of truth was on His lips, and the world was at His back. He stood as if He would plead for men, and a crown of gold hung near His head.

Christian: "What does this mean?"

Interpreter: "I have shown you this picture first, for this is He Who is to be your sole guide when you can not find your way to the land to which you go. Listen carefully to what I tell you, for you will meet some who will pretend to lead you right; but their way goes down to death."

The Large Room

Then he took him to a large room that was full of dust, and Interpreter told his servant to sweep it. Now when he did so, such clouds of dust flew up that Christian began to cough.

Then said Interpreter to a young girl who stood by, "Put water on the floor so the dust will not rise." When she had done this, it was easy to sweep the floor.

Christian: "What means this?"

The Law and the Book

Interpreter: "This room is the heart of the man who knows not the grace of God. The dust is his sin. He who swept first is the Law, but the Law can not take away sin. She who put water on the floor is the Book which tells Good News to Man. Now as soon as the Law swept, the dust flew about so much that the room could not be made clean by him. This is to show you that the Law as it works does not cleanse the heart from sin. The Law only stirs sin up so that we can see it more clearly.

"Then you saw the young girl come in to put water on the dust. This shows that sin is made clean by faith in the Book."

The Little Room

Then Interpreter led Christian to a little room where two children sat. One child was named Passion, and one was named Patience. Patience was happy and quiet, but Passion was pouting.

"What is wrong with Passion?" Christian asked.

"His mother wants him to wait until next year for some presents," Interpreter said, "but he wants all the good things right now. Patience is happy because she is willing to wait."

Passion's Rags

Then someone came to Passion and gave him a box full of wonderful gifts. Passion played with them for awhile, but soon he had broken them all or thrown them away. He was left at the end with nothing but rags.

"What does this mean?" Pilgrim asked.

Interpreter: "Passion is like the people of this world. They want all the good things now. They do not care what happens to them when they are older. They do not care what happens to them after they die. Soon they will have nothing but rags.

Patience's Wisdom

"Patience is wise. She thinks about Heaven. She is willing to wait for the best gifts. She will have wonderful things when Passion is left with nothing."

"Now," said Christian, "let me go on my way."

"Good," said Interpreter. "Remember all that I have told you, and may faith guide thee!"

Thinking It Through

1. Who was the man in the picture? How would He help Christian?

2. What does the Law do?

3. What does the young girl sprinkling water represent?

4. In the end who was happier, Passion or Patience? Why?

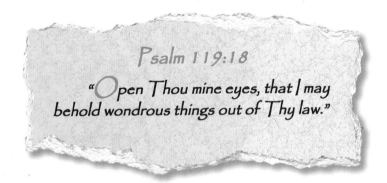

Psalm 119:18

"Open Thou mine eyes, that I may behold wondrous things out of Thy law."

Chapter 9

hen I saw in my dream that the high-way where Christian was to walk had a wall on each side, and the name of that wall was Salvation. Christian ran up this highway, still struggling under the burden on his back. At the top of the hill stood a cross, and at the foot of it a tomb. Just as Christian came up to the cross, his burden slid from his back and fell into the tomb, and I saw it no more.

Joy and Tears

Then was Christian glad, and he said with a merry heart, "He gives me rest by His grief and life by His death."

---

seal—a piece of wax used to seal a letter or a scroll
bound—held to
sloth—laziness; slowness
presumption—blind confidence; passing beyond the ordinary bounds of good behavior
formalist—one who pays close attention to forms and ceremonies in religion but misses the true meaning of worship
hypocrisy (hĭ·päk′rə·sē)—pretending to be what one is not
vain-glory—excessive vanity or conceit; boastfulness
timorous—timid; meek; afraid
mistrust—disbelief

Yet he stood still for awhile, for he was struck with awe to think that the sight of the cross should take away his burden. Three or four times did he look on the cross and the tomb, and the tears rose to his eyes.

As he stood thus and wept, three Bright Ones came to him. One of them said, "Peace be to thee! Thy sins are forgiven." Another came up to him to take off his rags and put a new robe on him. The third set a mark on his face, and gave him a scroll with a seal on it. "Look on this as you run," he said, "and give it in at the Celestial Gate."

Christian's Song

Christian gave three leaps for joy and sang as he went. "Ah, what a place is this! Here did the strings crack that bound my burden to me. Blessed cross! Blessed tomb! Nay, blessed is the Lord that was put to shame for me!"

 The Sleepers

He went on thus until he came to a valley. There he saw three men who were sleeping with chains on their feet. The name of one was Simple, one Sloth, and the third Presumption. As Christian saw them lie in this state, he went to wake them. "You are like those that sleep on the top of a mast," he said, "for the Dead Sea is at your feet. Wake, rise, and come with me. Trust me, and I will help you get rid of your chains."

With that they looked up at him, and Simple said, "You do not look strong enough to help us." Sloth said, "I want to get more sleep." Presumption said, "Let us do as we please." And so they lay down to sleep once more.

The Thieves

Then I saw in my dream that two men jumped from the top of the wall and made great haste to come up to Christian. Their names were Formalist and Hypocrisy.

Formalist and Hypocrisy: "We were born in the land of Vain-glory and are on our way to Mount Zion for praise."

Christian: "Why came you not in at the Gate? Do you not know that he that does not come in at the door, but climbs up some other way, is a thief?"

"To go through the gate is too far around," they answered. "The best way is to make a short cut of it and climb the wall, as we have done."

Christian: "But what will the Lord of the town to which we are bound think of it, if we go not in the way He tells us?"

"You do not need to worry about that," they said. "People have been climbing over this wall for years."

The Right Way

"But," said Christian, "is that the right way to get in?"

"What difference does it make?" they asked. "We are in. You came in the gate and we came in over the wall. You just think you are better than we are."

Christian: "I walk by the rule of my Lord, but you walk by the rule of your own wishes. The Lord of the way will treat you like thieves in the end."

The Hill of Difficulty

They all went on until they came to the foot of the

Hill of Difficulty, where there was a spring. Two more paths led from that place, one on the left hand and one on the right. But the path that Christian was told to take went straight up the hill, and the name of the hill was Difficulty.

When Christian got as far as the Spring of Life, he drank of it and then went up the hill.

But when the two men saw that it was steep and high, and that there were three ways to choose from, they decided not to take the difficult way. One of them took the path called Danger and lost his way in a great wood. The other went by the road of Destruction. This road led him to a wide field full of dark rocks, where he fell and rose no more.

The Park

I then saw Christian go up the hill. At first I could see him run, then walk, and then go on his hands and knees, so steep was it. Halfway up was a park made by the Lord of the hill, that those who came by might rest there.

So here Christian sat down, took out the scroll, and read it.

At last he fell asleep, and while he slept his scroll fell from his hand. After he had slept a long time, a man came up to him and woke him, saying, "Go to the ant, thou sluggard; consider her ways, and be wise."

 ## The Awakening

At this Christian gave a start, and went on his way as fast as he could.

When he had got near to the top of the hill, two men, whose names were Timorous and Mistrust, ran up to meet him.

"Sirs, what's the matter?" Christian called to them. "You run the wrong way!"

 ## The Cowards

"We were going to the City of Zion," said Timorous. "But the farther we go, the more danger we meet with. Therefore, we turned around, and are going back."

"Yes," said Mistrust. "Just in front of us we saw two lions on our path. We did not know if they were awake or asleep, but we thought that they would catch us and tear us in pieces."

 ## Fear

Christian: "You make me afraid. But where can I go to be safe? If I go back to the City of Destruction, I am sure to lose my life; but if I can get to the Celestial City, there shall I be safe. To turn back is death. To go on is fear of death, and everlasting life beyond it. I will yet go forward."

So Mistrust and Timorous ran down the hill and Christian went on his way.

Thinking It Through

1. What happened to Christian's burden?

2. Why did Christian refuse to listen to Formalist and Hypocrisy? Do you think that Christian was wise? Why?

3. What happened to Formalist and Hypocrisy?

4. What happened as a result of Christian's sleeping?

5. Why were the two cowards coming back? What would you have done if you had seen the lions?

2 Timothy 1:7

"For God hath not given us the spirit of fear; but of power, and of love, and of a sound mind."

Chapter 10

As Christian went on, he thought once more of what he had heard from Timorous and Mistrust. Then he felt in his cloak for his scroll so that he might read it and find some peace. He felt for it but found it not. Then was Christian in great distress, and he knew not what to do. He had lost the scroll which could give him such comfort.

At last he thought, "I slept in the park by the side of the hill." So he fell down on his knees and asked God to forgive him for sleeping when he should have been working. Then he went back to look for his scroll. But as he went, he told himself over and over how foolish he had been. "Oh, fool that I am!" said he, "to sleep in the daytime! The Lord of the hill made that park for rest, but not for laziness."

---

distress—trouble; a state of danger or desperate need
vain—unsuccessful; useless; empty; conceited
watchful—careful; alert; attentive
hesitate—to hold back; to pause for a moment

lodge—a small house belonging to a servant
graceless—not having or experiencing God's grace
discretion (dĭs·krĕsh′ən)— the ability to judge what is right or wrong

Regret

With tears and sighs he went back, and with much care he looked on this side and on that for his scroll. After a time he came near to the cave where he had sat and slept. "How far," thought Christian, "have I gone in vain! Such was the lot of the Jews for their sin; they were sent back by the way of the Red Sea. And I am made to walk those steps with grief which I might have walked with joy, if only I had not been lazy. How far might I have been on my way by this time! I am made to walk those steps three times which I should only have walked once. And now, too, I am likely to be lost in the night, for the day is almost over. O that I had not slept!"

Joy

Now by this time he had come to the park once more. For a while he sat down and wept, but at last, as he cast a sad glance at the foot of the bench, he saw his scroll. He caught it up with haste and put it into his cloak.

Words are too weak to tell the joy of Christian when he found his scroll. He put it into the breast of his coat and gave thanks to God. With what a light step did he now climb the hill!

The Beautiful Palace

But before he got to the top, the sun went down on Christian, and he was alone in the dark. Still he went on, and while he thought of his problem he looked up and saw a great palace in front of him. The name of the palace was Beautiful, and it stood beside the highway. Christian hurried on, hoping that he could rest there awhile.

As he started to turn toward the doorway of the house, he saw something that made him tremble. Two huge lions stood in the way!

The Lions

"Now what shall I do?" thought Pilgrim. "I see now why Timorous and Mistrust were driven back."

Just then Watchful, the man who kept the door of the palace, came out. When he saw that Christian

hesitated, he came out to him and said, "Is thy strength so small? Fear not the two wild beasts. They are bound by chains, and are put here to try the faith of those that have it, and to discover those that have none. Keep in the middle of the path and no harm shall come to thee."

Dread

Then I saw, in my dream, that still he went on in great dread of the wild beasts. He heard them roar, yet they did him no harm. He got by them and went on with joy until he came and stood in front of the lodge where Watchful lived.

Christian: "Sir, what house is this? May I rest here tonight?"

The Lord of the Hill

Watchful: "This house was built by the Lord of the Hill to give aid to those who climb up it for the good cause. Tell me, where do you come from?"

Christian: "I am come from the City of Destruction, and am on my way to Mount Zion. But the day is far spent, and I would, with your leave, pass the night here."

Watchful: "What is your name?"

Christian: "My name is now Christian, but at first it was Graceless."

Watchful: "How is it you came so late? The sun is set."

Christian then told him why it was.

Discretion

Watchful: "Well, I will call one that lives here. If she likes your talk, she will let you come in, for these are the rules of the house."

Then he rang a bell. At the sound of the bell there came out at the door a grave and fair maid whose name was Discretion. When Watchful told her why Christian had come there, she said, "What is your name?"

"It is Christian," said he, "and I greatly wish to rest here tonight. I see that this place was built by the Lord of the Hill to protect from harm those who come to it."

So she gave a smile, but the tears stood in her eyes. In a short time she said, "I will go get my sisters."

Thinking It Through

1. What did Christian not see concerning the lions?

2. Do you ever have problems that are like lions? If you are saved, what can you know about all your problems?

3. What was Christian's old name?

4. Who built the beautiful palace? Why? What does this show you about God?

1 Corinthians 10:13

"There hath no temptation taken you but such as is common to man: but God is faithful, Who will not suffer you to be tempted above that ye are able; but will with the temptation also make a way to escape, that ye may be able to bear it."

Chapter 11

Discretion ran to the door and brought in Prudence, Piety, and Charity. "Come in, thou who art blessed of the Lord," they said. "This house was built by the King of the Hill for such as you." Then Christian bent down his head and went with them to the house.

Piety: "Come, good Christian. Tell us about all the things that have happened to you in your travels."

---

prudence—carefulness or caution in making decisions
piety—reverence toward God
flight—a running away; fleeing; escaping
slew—killed
feat—a deed; an accomplishment
delectable—delightful; charming

Immanuel (ĭ·mǎn′yōō·wəl)— a name given to Jesus, the Messiah
humiliation (hyōō·mǐl′ē·ā′shən)— the act of damaging a person's dignity or importance

Christian: "With a very good will, and I am glad that you should ask it of me."

Christian's Tale

Prudence: "First, tell us what it is that makes you wish so much to go to Mount Zion."

Christian: "Why, there I hope to see Him that died on the Cross. There I hope to get rid of all those things that make me sad and afraid. There, they say, is no death, and there I shall dwell with such as love the Lord."

Charity: "Do you have a wife and children?"

Christian: "Yes, I do."

Charity: "And why did you not bring them with you?"

Christian's Sorrow

Christian then wept, and said, "Oh, how glad I would have been to do so! But they would not come with me, and they did not want me to leave them."

Charity: "And did you pray that God would help them to want to go with you?"

Christian: "Yes, I prayed much about that, for my wife and children are very dear to me."

Christian's Peace

Christian talked with these friends until it grew dark. Then he was led to a large room, the name of which was Peace. There he slept until break of day, and when he awoke, he sang a hymn.

The sisters told him that he should not leave until they had shown him all the interesting things that were in that place. They showed to him the rod of Moses, the lamps with which Gideon put to flight the host of Midian, and the ox goad with which Shamgar slew his foes. They brought out the jawbone of an ass with which Samson did such great feats, and the sling and stone with which David slew Goliath.

Then I saw in my dream that Christian rose to leave Discretion, Prudence, Piety, and Charity. But they said that he must stay until the next day, because they wanted to show him the Delectable Mountains. They took him to the top of the house and bade him look to the south. When he did this, he saw, a great way off, a rich land full of hills, woods, vines, shrubs, and streams.

Immanuel's Land

"What is the name of this land?" asked Christian. The sisters told him it was Immanuel's Land.

"And," said they, "it is as much meant for you, and the like of you, as this hill is. When you reach the place, there you may see the gate of the Celestial City." Then they gave him a sword, and put on him armor which covered him from head to foot, lest he should meet some enemy in the way. Then they went with him down the hill.

"Of a truth," said Christian, "it is as difficult to come down the hill as it was to go up."

The Valley of Humiliation

Prudence: "So it is, for it is a hard thing for a man to go down to the Valley of Humiliation, as you are doing now, and for this cause we have come with you to the foot of the hill." Although he went with great care, he slipped once or twice.

Then in my dream I saw that when they had reached the foot of the hill, these good friends of Christian's gave him a loaf of bread, a bottle of water, and a cluster of raisins. Then they left him to go on his way.

Thinking It Through

1. What are the names of Discretion's three sisters?

2. How did Christian feel about leaving his family behind?

3. What will Christian be able to see in Immanuel's Land?

4. What valley was extremely difficult to climb down into?

Philippians 3:13–14

"... Forgetting those things which are behind, and reaching forth unto those things which are before,

"I press toward the mark for the prize of the high calling of God in Christ Jesus."

Chapter 12

Christian had not been alone for long before he saw a terrible enemy named Apollyon coming to meet him. Then did Christian fear, and he wondered whether he should go back or stand his ground. But Christian thought that since he had no armor on his back, if he were to turn around, Apollyon could pierce him from behind. Therefore he stood his ground, and Apollyon met him with looks of scorn.

 ## Questions

Apollyon: "Where do you come from, and where are you going?"

Christian: "I came from the City of Destruction, which is the place of all sin, and I am on my way to Zion."

Apollyon (ə·päl′yən)—a name for Satan
pierce—to cut or puncture with a pointed object
realm—area; region
vow—a solemn promise
beware—to look out for; to be cautious

holy—excellent; pure; spiritually perfect
boast—brag
reel—to turn or move round and round; to whirl

Apollyon: "By this I see that you are mine, for I am the Prince of all that land. How is it, then, that you have left your king? If I did not have a hope that you may do me more good, I would strike you to the ground with one blow."

Christian: "I was born in your realm, it is true, but you are a hard master, and no man could live on your wages."

Apollyon's Promise

Apollyon: "No prince likes to lose his followers, and I do not want to lose you. So if you will come back, I promise to make you rich."

Christian: "But I am bound by vows to the King of Kings. How can I in fairness go back with you?"

Apollyon: "You have changed, it seems, from bad to worse. Why not give Him the slip, and come back with me?"

Christian's Promise

Christian: "I gave Him my faith, and promised to be true to Him. How can I go back from this?"

Apollyon: "You did the same to me, and yet I am willing to forget that if you will just come back to me."

"No," said Pilgrim. "I love my new Master. I am His servant, and I will follow Him."

Apollyon broke out in a great rage and said, "I hate that Prince, and I hate His laws, and I am come out to stop you."

 ## The Battle

Christian: "Beware what you do. I am on the King's highway, the way of holiness."

Apollyon: "I have no fear. Prepare yourself to die." With that he threw a dart of fire at his breast, but Christian caught it with his shield. Then Christian drew his sword and fought as hard as he could. Apollyon threw darts as thick as hail and, in spite of all that Christian could do, wounded him in his head, his hand, and his foot.

This made Christian pause in the fight for a time, but Apollyon still came on, and Christian once more took heart. They fought for half a day, until Christian, weak from his wounds, could hardly stand. When Apollyon saw this, he threw him down with great force, and Christian's sword fell out of his hand. Then said Apollyon, "I am sure of thee now."

Christian's Victory

Christian thought sure that he would die now, but he reached down, grabbed his sword, and cried, "Boast not, O Apollyon!" And with that he struck Apollyon a blow which made him reel back as one who had been wounded unto death. Then he spread out his dragon wings and flew away, so that Christian for a time saw him no more.

Christian said, "I will now give thanks to Him that hath delivered me out of the mouth of the lion; to Him that did help me against Apollyon." Then there came to him a hand which held some of the leaves of the tree of life. Christian took some of them, and as soon as he had put them to his wounds, they were healed.

Thinking It Through

1. Who is Apollyon?

2. Why did Apollyon say that he was Christian's master?

3. What did Apollyon promise Christian if he would turn back?

4. Where was Christian wounded?

5. What healed Christian's wounds?

Romans 8:37
1 John 5:4

"Nay, in all these things we are more than conquerors through Him that loved us."

"For whatsoever is born of God overcometh the world: and this is the victory that overcometh the world, even our faith."

Chapter 13

Now near this place was the Valley of the Shadow of Death, and Christian had to go through it to get to the Celestial City. It was a land of deserts and pits, a land that none but a Christian could pass through, and where no man lived.

So as we shall soon see, he was worse off here than in his fight with Apollyon.

The Two Men

As he drew near the Shadow of Death, he met with two men. "Where are you going?" Christian asked them.

---

doth (dŭth)—does
dwell—to stay or abide

creature—a living thing
reassurance—restored confidence

Men: "Back! Back! and we would have you do the same if you prize life and peace."

Christian: "But why?"

Men: "We went on as far as we dared."

Christian: "What then have you seen?"

The Warning

Men: "Seen! Why, the Valley of the Shadow of Death. But by good luck we caught sight of what lay in front of it before we came up. Death doth spread out his wings there. In a word it is a place full of bad men, where no law dwells."

Christian: "But this is my way to Zion."

Men: "Be it thy way then; we will not choose it for ours."

So they took their leave and Christian went on, but still with his drawn sword in his hand, for fear lest he should meet once more with a foe.

The Ditch

I saw then in my dream that as far as this valley went, there ran on the right hand a deep ditch. It was that ditch to which the blind have led the blind as long as the world has been made. And lo, on the left hand there was quicksand, in which if a man fall, he will find no firm ground for his foot to stand on. The pathway was not broad, which made it even harder for Christian. The quicksand went on for miles, and in the middle of the valley was a deep pit.

"Now," thought Christian, "what shall I do?"

All-Prayer

Flames and smoke came up from the pit, almost to Christian's feet, and he could hear terrible noises. His sword would do no good against these enemies. Now he began to use another weapon, called "All-Prayer." He cried, "Make haste, O God, to deliver me; make haste to help me, O Lord."

He went on for miles and miles, and still the flames kept leaping toward him, and the voices grew louder and more terrible. Sometimes he thought he should turn around and go back. At these times, he thought of the other dangers his Lord had helped him through. He knew that He would help him now, too. "I will walk in the strength of the Lord God," Christian called in a loud voice.

A Creature Speaks

I saw one thing in my dream which I must not leave out. As Christian walked near the mouth of the pit, a creature stepped out of it and whispered bad things to him and took God's name in vain.

Christian thought these things must have come from his own mind. This troubled him more than anything he had met before. To think that he should take that name in vain for which he felt so deep a love was a great grief to him. Yet there was no help for it.

Christian did not know that it was really the creature from the pit who spoke the words.

Christian's Reassurance

Then he thought he heard a voice saying, "Though I walk through the Valley of the Shadow of Death, I will fear no evil, for Thou art with me."

Now Christian was glad for three reasons. Someone else who loved God was going through that valley. He was reminded that God was with them, even in that dark and frightening place. And he had hope that he would catch up with the man ahead of him and have company for his journey.

Reunion

As Christian went on, he found there was a rise in the road, which had been made on purpose that pilgrims might see what lay ahead. Up this road Christian went, and he saw his old friend Faithful a short way off.

Then said Christian, "Hello, friend. Wait a minute, and I will join you."

Christian caught up with Faithful, and they spoke of all that had come to pass since they had last met.

Thinking It Through

1. Why did Christian have to pass through the Valley of the Shadow of Death?

2. What made the journey through the valley so difficult?

3. What weapon did Christian use to help him through the valley? What can we do when we have problems?

4. Who was really responsible for the evil sayings Christian heard?

Psalm 27:1–2

"The Lord is my light and my salvation; whom shall I fear? the Lord is the strength of my life; of whom shall I be afraid?"

"When the wicked, even mine enemies and my foes, came upon me to eat up my flesh, they stumbled and fell."

Chapter 14

In course of time the road brought Christian and his friend Faithful to a town called Vanity. There is a fair there all year long, and all that is bought or sold there is vain and worthless to God. Yet he who wants to go to the Celestial City has to pass through this fair.

As soon as Christian and Faithful came to the town, a crowd drew around them. Some said they were crazy because they did not dress and speak the way the townspeople did, and they were not interested in the things for sale in Vanity Fair. When Christian spoke, his words drew from these folks fierce taunts and jeers. Soon there was such a stir that the chief man of the fair sent his friends to arrest these two strange men.

---

vanity—anything that is worthless

taunts—insulting words; sarcastic remarks

jeers—mocking or scornful remarks or sounds

strife—a fight; a struggle

superstition—a belief based on ignorance or fear

doom—condemnation; death; ruin

jury—a group of people whose job it is to decide the outcome of a trial

malice—extreme ill-will; a desire to harm another

 Taunts and Jeers

"Why do you dress so strangely?" the man asked them. "Why do you not talk the way we do? Why do you not want to buy the things that we sell?"

"We are pilgrims and strangers in this world," said Christian. "We wear the clothes that please our Lord. We speak words that make Him glad. We are on our way to Zion, and we have no desire for the things of this world. We have done nothing to hurt you. Please, let us be on our way."

Blows and Fights

But those who were judging the case thought that they must have come to cause trouble at the fair, so they beat them with sticks and put them into a cage that all the men at the fair might laugh at them. Then they began to throw rocks at them. But Christian and Faithful spoke kindly to those who were so mean to them, and some of the people began to take their side. This led to blows and fights, and the blame was laid on Christian and Faithful, who were then made to walk up and down the fair in chains. Finally, faint with being beaten, they were set with their feet in the stocks. But even this they bore with joy, for they knew that all would be well in the end.

The Trial

By and by they were taken to court for a trial. The name of the judge was Lord Hate-good. They were charged with having come to Vanity Fair to spoil its trade and to stir up strife in the town.

Faithful said to the Judge, "I am a man of peace, and the only thing that I fight is Sin. The prince of this city is Beelzebub, and I hate him."

Some stood up for Faithful because they

knew his words were true and right, but the judge said, "Anyone who knows about this man may speak."

 Three Witnesses

So three men, whose names were Envy, Superstition, and Pick-thank, stood up and swore to speak the truth, and to tell what they knew about Faithful. Envy said, "My lord, this man does not care about kings or laws, but seeks to spread his own views, and to teach men what he calls faith. I heard him say just now that the ways of our town are evil. Can we let him talk about us like that?"

Then Superstition said, "My lord, I know not much of this man, and I have no wish to know more. But of this I am sure: that he is a bad man, for he says that the way we worship is wrong."

Pick-thank was then told to say what he knew. "My Lord," he said, "I have known this man for a long time, and I have heard him say things that should not be said. He speaks against our great Prince Beelzebub, and says that we should not listen to him. More than this, he has been heard to criticize you, my Lord, who are now his judge."

Then said the Judge to Faithful, "You wicked man! Hast thou heard what these good folk have said about thee?

Faithful: "May I speak a few words for myself?"

Judge: "Thy just doom would be to die on the spot; still, let us hear what thou hast to say."

Faithful's Testimony

Faithful: "I say, then, to Mr. Envy, that all ways of life in which men do not listen to the Word of God are full of sin. As to the charge of Mr. Superstition, nothing can save us if we do not come to God by way of the Cross. To Mr. Pick-thank, I say that men should flee from the Prince of this town and his friends, as they would flee from the wrath to come. And so, I pray that the Lord will help me."

Then the Judge said, "You see this man who has made such a stir in our town. You have heard what these good men have said of him, which he admits to be true. Now you must decide whether to save his life or hang him."

The Jury's Decision

The twelve men on the jury whispered to each

other. "This man just wants to cause trouble," said Mr. Blind-man. "Out of the world with him!" said Mr. No-good.

"I hate to even look at him," said Mr. Malice. "From the first I could not bear him," said Mr. Love-ease. "Nor I, for he would be sure to blame my ways," said Mr. Live-loose.

"Hang him, hang him!" said Mr. Heady. "A low wretch!" said Mr. High-mind. "I long to crush him," said Mr. Enmity.

"He is a rascal," said Mr. Liar. "Death is too good for him," said Mr. Cruelty. "Let us kill him, so he will be out of the way," said Mr. Hate-light.

Mr. Implacable then said, "Not to gain all the world would I make peace with him, so let us doom him to death."

Faithful's Death

And so they did, and in a short time he was led back to the prison and put to the worst death that could be thought of.

Now I saw that there stood near the crowd a chariot with two bright horses, which, as soon as his enemies had killed him, took Faithful up through the clouds straight to the Celestial City.

Thinking It Through

1. What did the crowd think of the two pilgrims? What does the world generally think about Christians?

2. Why were Christian and Faithful blamed for the fights?

3. Do you think the jury was fair?

4. What happened to Faithful after he was put to death?

James 1:12

"Blessed is the man that endureth temptation: for when he is tried, he shall receive the crown of life, which the Lord hath promised to them that love Him."

Chapter 15

As for Christian, he was set free, and there came to join him a man named Hopeful. This man had seen that Christian and Faithful were different from the others, and he, too, wanted to be a Christian. Thus, while one lost his life for the truth, a new man rose from his death to walk the same way with Christian. Hopeful said that there were other men in Vanity Fair who would become Christians before long because of the testimony of Christian and Faithful.

 ## Their Song

By and by their way lay by the bank of a pure stream, from which they drank. On each side of it were green trees that bore fruit, and in a field through which it ran they lay down to sleep. When they woke

---

hopeful—having hope; expecting to achieve or receive something in the future
meadow—a large field or grassland
stile—a set of steps used for passing over a fence
vain-confidence—a confidence having no firm foundation

up they sat for awhile in the shade of the trees. They
went on like this for three or four days,
and to pass the time they sang:

> "He that can tell
> What sweet fresh fruit
>   and leaves these trees
>   do yield,
> Will soon sell all, that
>   he may buy this field."

By-path Meadow

Now on the left hand of the road was By-path
Meadow, a fair green field with a path through it and
a stile. "Come, good Hopeful," said Christian, "let us
walk on the grass."

Hopeful: "But what if this path should lead us
wrong?"

Christian: "How can it? Look, doth it not go
along beside the highway?"

Vain-confidence

So they set off through the field. But they had
not gone far when they saw in front of them a man,
Vain-confidence by name, who told them that the
path led to the Celestial Gate. So the man went first;

but lo, the night came on, and it grew so dark that they lost sight of their guide. Because Vain-confidence did not see the path in front of him, he fell into a deep pit and was heard of no more.

 ## The Wrong Path

"Where are we now?" asked Hopeful.

Christian did not answer. "I have led my friend in the wrong way," he thought. Now the lightning began to flash, and rain came down in streams.

Hopeful (with a groan): "Oh, that I had stayed on the right path!"

Christian: "Who could have thought that this path should lead us wrong?"

Hopeful: "I was afraid of it from the first, and so were you."

Christian: "Good friend, I am sorry that I have led you away from the right path."

Hopeful: "Say no more. No doubt it is for our good."

Christian: "We must not stand here talking. Let us try to go back."

Hopeful: "But, good Christian, let me go first."

Then they heard a voice say, "Set thine heart toward the highway, the way thou hast been, turn once more." But by this time the stream was deep from the rain that fell, and to go back did not seem safe. Yet they went back, though it was so dark and the stream ran so high that once or twice they thought they would drown. But no matter how hard they tried, they could not get back

that night. So they found a little shelter from the rain, and there they slept until the break of day.

Thinking It Through

1. Who was Christian's new friend?

2. Why was Faithful's death helpful?

3. Why did Christian and Hopeful get into trouble?

4. Why do we sometimes get into trouble?

Ephesians 5:15, 16

"See then that ye walk circumspectly, not as fools, but as wise,

"Redeeming the time, because the days are evil."

Chapter 16

Now, not far from the place where they lay was Doubting Castle. The lord of this castle was Giant Despair, and it was on his ground that they now slept. Giant Despair found them there, and with a gruff voice he woke them up.

"Where did you come from?" he asked. "And what brought you here?"

They told him that they had lost the path. Then said Giant Despair, "You have no right to force your way in here; the ground on which you lie is mine."

---

despair—loss of hope or confidence
gruff—rough; deep; harsh
dungeon—a dark underground prison
stout—bulky; solid; strong

misery—a state of suffering and discomfort
fierce—extremely furious or wild in appearance
threat—a promise to cause damage or injury

 The Dungeon

They had not much to say, as they knew that they had done wrong. So Giant Despair drove them on and put them into a dark and dirty dungeon in Doubting Castle. Here they were kept for three days, and they had no light nor food, nor a drop to drink all that time.

Now Giant Despair told his wife what he had done. "What will be the best way to treat them?" he asked her.

The Beating

"Beat them well," said the wife. So he took a stout stick from a crab tree and went down to the dungeon where poor Christian and Hopeful lay. He beat them as if they were dogs. He beat them so hard that they could not even move, and they spent all that day in sighs and tears.

The next day Giant Despair came once more, and he found them sore from the beating. "There is no chance that I will ever let you go," he told them. "The best thing for you to do is to end your own lives, for what is the sense of going on living in this misery?"

"We still have hope that you will let us go," they replied.

With that he sprang up with a fierce look, and no doubt would have killed them, but that he fell into a fit for a time and lost the use of his hand. So he drew back and left them to think of what he had said.

Questions and Answers

Christian: "Friend, what shall we do? The life that we now lead is worse than death. For my part I know not which is best—to live in this dungeon, or to kill myself. I feel that even the grave would be a happier place than this dungeon. Shall we let Giant Despair rule us?"

Hopeful: "In good truth our case is a sad one, and to die would be more sweet to me than to live here. Yet let us bear in mind that the Lord of that land to which we go hath said, "Thou shalt not kill." God is still the ruler of all things. Who knows but that God, Who made the world, may cause Giant Despair to die or lose the use of his hands as he did at first. I have made up my mind to be brave and to try to get away from this place. I was a fool not to get away the first time he came to the dungeon. But let us not put an end to our own lives, for good may come of this yet."

By these words Hopeful helped Christian to change his mind.

Christian Faints

Well, at night the Giant went down to the cell to see if they were still alive. They were alive, but just barely. Because of their wounds and lack of food, they could not do much more than breathe.

When Giant Despair found they were not dead, he fell into a great rage and said that it should be worse with them than if they had not been born. At this they shook with fear, and Christian fainted.

Hopeful's Encouragement

When he came to, Hopeful said, "My friend, think of how strong in faith you have been until now. Say, could Apollyon hurt you, or all that you heard, or saw, or felt in the Valley of the Shadow of Death? Look at the fears, the griefs, the woes that you have gone through. And now to be cast down! I, too, am in this cell, far more weak a man than you, and Giant Despair beat me as well as you, and keeps me from food and light. Let us both bear up as well as we can."

When night came on, the wife of Giant Despair said to him, "Well, will the two men yield?"

"No," he answered, "they choose to stand firm, and they will not put an end to their lives."

The Graves

Then said the wife, "At dawn take them to the yard, show them the graves of all those 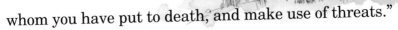 whom you have put to death, and make use of threats."

So Giant Despair took them to this place and said, "In ten days' time you shall be thrown in here if you do not yield. Go; get you down to your den once more." With that he beat them all the way back, and there they lay the whole day.

Now, when night was come, Giant Despair's wife said, "I fear much that these men live on hoping that they can pick the lock of the cell and get free."

"Do you think so, my dear?" said Giant Despair to his wife. "Then at sunrise I will search them."

 ## The Key

Now, that night, as Christian and Hopeful lay in the den, they fell on their knees to pray. They prayed until the day broke. Then Christian gave a start and said, "What a fool I am to lie in this dark den when I might be a free man! I have a key in my pocket, the name of which is God's Promise. I feel sure that it will turn the lock of all the doors in Doubting Castle."

Then said Hopeful, "That is good news. Get it out, and let us try it."

 Freedom

So Christian put the key in the lock. The bolt sprang back, the door flew wide, and Christian and Hopeful both came out. When they got to the yard door, the key did just as well. But the lock of the last strong gate of Doubting Castle was hard to turn. Yet it did turn at last, though the hinge gave so loud a creak that it woke up Giant Despair, who rose in anger to look for the two men.

A Warning

But just then he felt his limbs fail, for a fit came upon him so that he could not reach their cell. Christian and Hopeful now fled back to the highway and were safe. When they sat down to rest on the stile, they said they would warn others who might come on this road. So they wrote these words on a post: "This is the way to Doubting Castle, which is kept by Giant Despair, who loves not the King of the Celestial Country, and who seeks to kill all who would go there."

Thinking It Through

1. Why did Christian and Hopeful not complain to God about what had happened to them?

2. What did Giant Despair want the two pilgrims to do? Why didn't they do this?

3. What helps Christians get out of problems? When we have problems, we can do the same thing. Where can we find God's promises?

4. What are some of the promises of God that can help you today?

Isaiah 40:31

"But they that wait upon the Lord shall renew their strength; they shall mount up with wings as eagles; they shall run, and not be weary; and they shall walk, and not faint."

Chapter 17

hen they came to the Delectable Mountains, which the Lord of the Hill owns. Here they saw gardens and orchards, vines, shrubs, woods, and streams. They drank and washed themselves, and they ate freely of the grapes.

Now there were shepherds at the tops of these hills, and as they stood by the highway, Christian and Hopeful spoke to the men. "Who owns these Delectable Mountains, and who owns the sheep that feed on them?"

---

sincere—honest; pure; true
error—a mistake; a departure from the truth
brink—the edge at the top of a steep place
caution—careful forethought to avoid danger
enchanted—under a spell; under the influence of charms

Men: "These hills are Immanuel's, and the sheep are His, too. He laid down His life for them."

Christian: "Is this the way to the Celestial City?"

Men: "You are on the right road."

Christian: "How far is it?"

Men: "Too far for all but those that shall get there, in good truth."

Christian: "Is the way safe?"

Men: "Safe for those who come in the right way, but the men of sin shall fall there."

Christian: "Is there a place of rest here for those who grow tired on the road?"

Men: "The Lord of these Hills told us to help all who came here, so the good things of the place are yours."

A Joyous Greeting

I then saw in my dream that the men said, "Where do you come from, and by what means have you traveled so far?"

When Christian and Hopeful had told their tale, the men cast a kind glance at them and said, "With joy we greet you on the Delectable Mountains!"

The names of the shepherds were Knowledge, Experience, Watchful, and Sincere. They led Christian and Hopeful by the hand to their tents and bade them eat of that which was there. Then they all went to their rest for the night.

Error

When the morning broke, the men woke up Christian and Hopeful and took them to a spot from which they could see a bright view on all sides. Then they went with the shepherds to the top of a high hill named Error. It was steep on the distant side, and they told them to look down to the foot of it. So Christian and Hopeful cast their eyes down and saw there some men who had lost their lives by a fall from the top. They were men who had been led wrong, for they had put their trust in false guides.

"Have you not heard of them?" said the men.

Christian: "Yes, I have."

Men: "These are they, and to this day they have not been put in a tomb, but they are left here to warn men to be careful not to come too near the brink of this hill."

Sobs and Tears

Then I saw that the shepherds led them to the top of Mount Caution and told them to look far off. "From that stile," said they, "there goes a path to Doubting Castle, which is kept by Giant Despair. The men whom you see wandering there came as you do now, until they got up to that stile. Then, as the right way was rough to walk in, they chose to go through a field, and there Giant Despair took them and shut them up in Doubting Castle. They were kept there in a den for a while, till he at last sent them out quite blind, and there they are still." At this Christian glanced over at Hopeful, and they both burst out with sobs and tears, but yet said not a word.

Then the four men took them up a high hill, the name of which was Clear, that they might see the gates of the Celestial City. They gave them a telescope to look through, but their hands shook, so they could not see well.

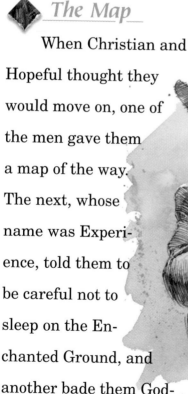

The Map

When Christian and Hopeful thought they would move on, one of the men gave them a map of the way. The next, whose name was Experience, told them to be careful not to sleep on the Enchanted Ground, and another bade them God-speed. Now it was that I awoke from my dream.

Thinking It Through

1. Christian and Hopeful found food and cleansing on the Delectable Mountains. By what book are we cleansed and fed? How?

2. What happened to other pilgrims that were captured by Giant Despair?

Psalm 16:11

"Thou wilt shew me the path of life: in Thy presence is fulness of joy; at Thy right hand there are pleasures for evermore."

Chapter 18

Then I slept and dreamed once more. This time I saw Christian and Hopeful go down near the foot of these hills toward the land of Conceit, which is connected to the highway by a small, crooked lane. Here they met a lad named Ignorance, to whom Christian said, "Where do you come from, and to what place do you go?"

Questions and Answers

Ignorance: "Sir, I was born in the land that lies off there on the left, and I wish to go to the Celestial City."

Christian: "How do you think you will get in at the gate?"

Ignorance: "The same way everyone else does."

---

conceit—loving or having a high opinion of self
ignorance (ĭg′nər·əns)—the state of lacking knowledge or an education
tithes—a tenth of one's money given to the Lord as an offering

Christian: "But what do you have to show at that gate that will allow you to pass through it?"

Ignorance: "I know my Lord's will, and I have led a good life. I pay for all that I have. I give tithes, and I give to the poor, and I have left my own land for that to which I now go."

The Small Lane

Christian: "But you did not come in at the gate that is at the head of this way. You came in through a small lane. I fear, though you may think well of all you have done, that when the time shall come, you will have this laid to your charge, that you are a thief— and so you will not get in."

Ignorance: "Well, I do not know you. You follow your own religion, and I will follow mine, and I hope all will be well. And as for the gate that you talk of, all the world knows that that is far from our land, and I do not think that there is a man in all our parts who does so much as know the way to it. I do not see what need there is that he should, since we have, as you see, a fine green lane at the next turn that comes down from our part of the world."

◆ Ignorance's Failure

Christian said in a low tone of voice to Hopeful, "There is more hope of a fool than of him."

Hopeful: "Let us pass on if you will and talk to him later. Maybe then he will listen."

So they went on, and Ignorance followed in their steps a short way behind them. They spoke to him again later, but he still would not listen, and he never did reach the Celestial City.

Thinking It Through

1. How do you think Ignorance got his name?

2. How did Ignorance hope to enter into the Celestial City? Can this get anyone into Heaven?

Titus 3:5

"Not by works of righteousness which we have done, but according to His mercy He saved us, by the washing of regeneration, and renewing of the Holy Ghost."

Chapter 19

t length they came to a land, the air of which made them sleepy. Here the lids of Hopeful's eyes dropped, and he said, "Let us lie down here and take a nap."

Christian: "By no means. If we sleep here, we will wake no more."

Hopeful: "Nay, friend Christian, sleep is sweet to the man who has worked all day."

 ## The Enchanted Ground

Christian: "Do you not remember that one of the shepherds told us to beware of the Enchanted Ground? He meant that we should be careful not to sleep. So let us not sleep, but watch."

Hopeful: "I see I am in the wrong."

Christian: "Now then, to keep sleep from our eyes, why don't you tell me how you first came to be a pilgrim?"

Beulah (byōō′lə)—a place of peace and rest
gem—a precious stone; jewel

Hopeful: "Do you mean how did I first come to look to the good of my soul?"

Christian: "Yes."

Hopeful's Tale

Hopeful: "For a long time the things that were seen and sold at Vanity Fair were a great joy to me."

Christian: "What things do you speak of?"

Hopeful: "All the things of this life: lying, swearing, drinking, love of self, and all that tends to kill the soul. But I heard from you and Faithful that the end of these things is death. That made me think that I wanted the new life that you have."

Thus did they talk as they went on their way.

The Land of Beulah

I saw in my dream that by this time Christian and Hopeful had gone through the Enchanted Ground and had come to the land of Beulah. There the air is sweet, and as their way lay through this land, they walked through it slowly. Here they heard the birds sing all day long, and the sun shone day and night. The Valley of Death was far away, and the land was out of the reach of Giant Despair. They could not from this place so much as see Doubting Castle.

Zion

Now they were in sight of Zion, and here some of the Bright Ones came to meet them. Here, too, they heard the voices of those who lived in Zion, and they had a good view of this land of joy. It was built of rare gems of all colors, and the streets were paved with gold.

At length, step by step, they drew near to Zion and saw that the gates were flung back.

A man stood in the way, to whom Christian and Hopeful said, "Whose vines and crops are these?"

"They are the King's," he said. "They were put there to give joy to those who travel on the road. Eat whatever fruit you like, and then come to see the King's walks."

I then saw that when they awoke from a good sleep, they wanted to go up to Zion. But the sun threw off such bright rays from the Celestial City, which was built of pure gold, that they could not as yet look on it except through a dark glass.

Thinking It Through

1. Why would it have been foolish for the Pilgrims to sleep?

2. Why were Hopeful's possessions useless?

Matthew 25:23

"His lord said unto him, Well done, good and faithful servant; thou hast been faithful over a few things, I will make thee ruler over many things: enter thou into the joy of thy lord."

Chapter 20

ow as they went, they met with two men in white robes, and the face of each shone bright as the light. These men said, "From where do you come?" When they had been told, they said, "You have but one thing more to do, which is a hard one, and then you will be in Zion."

Christian and Hopeful then begged the two men to go with them, which they did. "But," said they, "it is by your own faith that you must get into the city."

The River

Now between them and the gate was a broad and deep river. It had no bridge, and the sight of it made Christian and Hopeful so afraid that they could not move.

---

reunion—a reuniting, or bringing or coming together again
toil—labor; hard work
host—the keeper of an inn; a great number

But the men who went with them said, "You cannot come to the gate unless you go through this stream."

"Is there no way but this one to the gate?" said poor Christian.

"Yes," they answered, "but there have been only two men, Enoch and Elijah, who have gone by that path since the world was made."

Fear

When Christian and Hopeful looked at the stream once more, they felt their hearts sink with fear. Yet through it lay the way to Zion.

"Is the stream all of one depth?" asked Christian.

He was told that it was not, for he would find the stream more or less deep as he had faith in the King of the place.

So they set foot on the stream, but Christian gave a loud cry to his good friend Hopeful and said, "The waves close round my head, and I sink."

Then said Hopeful, "Be of good cheer; my feet feel the bottom of the stream, and it is good."

Christian's Despair

But Christian said, "Ah, Hopeful, the pains of death have got hold of me; I shall not reach the land that I long for." And with that a cloud came on his sight, so that he could not see.

Hopeful had a hard time keeping Christian's head above the water. At times Christian would sink out of sight, and then in a while he would rise up half dead.

Hopeful's Encouragement

Then said Hopeful, "My friend, all this is sent to see if you will remember all that God has done for you and trust Him with all your heart."

At these words Hopeful saw that Christian was in deep thought, so he said to him, "Be of good cheer. Christ will make thee whole."

Then Christian broke out with a loud voice, "Oh, I see Him, and He speaks to me and says, 'When you pass through the waters, I will be with you.' "

Victory

And now they both got strength, and the stream was as still as a stone. Christian felt the bed of it with his feet, and he could walk through it. Thus they got to the right bank, where the two men in bright robes stood waiting for them, and their clothes were left in the stream.

Now you must bear in mind that Zion was on a steep hill, yet Christian and Hopeful went up with ease and great speed, for they had these two men to lead them by the arms.

Zion, at Last!

The hill stood in the sky, for the base of it was there. So in sweet talk they went up through the air. The Bright Ones told them of the joy of the place. "Words can not tell enough about it," they said. "There you will see the Tree of Life and eat of the fruits of it."

 ## Reunion

"When you come there," said they, "white robes will be put on you, and your talk from day to day shall be with the King for all time. There you shall not see such things as you saw on earth, such as worry and hunger and pain and death. You now go to be with Abraham, Isaac, and Jacob."

Christian and Hopeful: "What will we do there?"

They said, "You will have rest for all your toil, and joy for all your grief. You will reap what you have sown—the fruit of all the tears you shed for the King by the way. In that place you will wear crowns of gold and be able at all times to see Him Who sits on the throne. There you shall serve Him with love, with shouts of joy, and with songs of praise."

 ## The Saints

Now, while they thus drew near to the gate, lo, a host of saints came to meet them. The two Bright Ones called to the saints, "These are men who felt love for our Lord when they were in the world. They left all for His name, and He sent us to bring them far on their way, that they might go in and look on their Lord with joy."

Then with great shouts the whole host came round on all sides, as if they wanted to guard them. It seemed to Christian and Hopeful as if all Zion had come down to meet them.

 ## Transformation

Now, when Christian and Hopeful went in at the gate, a great change took place in them. They were given robes that shone like gold. There were bright hosts that came with harps and crowns, and they said to them, "Enter ye into the joy of the Lord." And then I heard all the bells in Zion ring.

 ## A Vision

Now, just as the gates were flung back for the men to pass in, I had a sight of Zion. It shone like the sun. The ground was of gold, and those who dwelt there had love in their looks, crowns on their heads, and palms in their hands. With one voice they sent forth shouts of praise.

But the gates were now once more shut, and I wished that I, too, had gone in to share this joy. Then I awoke, and, lo, it was a dream.

Thinking It Through

1. What does going through the river mean?

2. Who were the only ones that did not go through the river?

3. Why did Christian nearly drown in the river?

4. What can we do to remove the clouds of doubt from our eyes?

5. Will the things that happened to Christian happen to us someday?

Revelation 21:1–2, 6–7

"And I saw a new heaven and a new earth: for the first heaven and the first earth were passed away; and there was no more sea.

"And I John saw the holy city, new Jerusalem, coming down from God out of heaven. . . .

"And He said unto me, It is done. I am Alpha and Omega, the beginning and the end. I will give unto him that is athirst of the fountain of the water of life freely.

"He that overcometh shall inherit all things; and I will be his God, and he shall be My son."

Chapter 21

 had another dream, this time about Christiana, the wife of Christian. She had been on her knees to pray. As she rose, she heard a loud knock at the door.

"If you come in God's name," said she, "come in."

 The Message

Then a man in robes as white as snow threw back the door and said, "Peace be to this house."

At a sight so new to her, Christiana at first grew pale with fear, but in a short time she took heart. "Where did you come from?" she asked. "And what do you want?"

"My name is Secret," he replied. "I dwell with those that are on high. Christiana, here is a note for thee, which I have brought from Christian."

---

mode—style; method; manner
rash—hasty; showing lack of caution
mercy—compassion; pity
lot—one's portion in life

hire—to employ; to provide work for
yearn—to long for
ail—to give pain or trouble to
in vain—uselessly; for nothing

So she took it, broke the seal, and read these words, which were in gold: "To her who was my dear wife. The King would have you do as I have done, for that was the way to come to His land and to dwell with Him in joy."

When Christiana read this, she shed tears. "Sir," she said, "will you take me and my sons with you? We, too, want to bow down to this King."

He answered gravely, "Christiana, the bitter is before the sweet. To reach the land where I dwell, you may have to go through troubles, as Christian did. Go to the Wicket Gate which stands in the head of the way, for there you must begin. I would have thee keep this letter with thee. Read it until thou hast learned it by heart. But thou must give it up at the last gate that leads to the Celestial City."

Christiana's Decision

Then Christiana spoke to her boys and said, "My sons, I have been sad lately at the death of Christian, your dear father. But I feel sure now that it is well with him and that he dwells in the land of life and peace. I have, too, felt deep grief at the thoughts of my own state and yours. We were wrong to let our hearts grow cold and to turn a deaf ear to your father in his time of trouble. We should have gone with him when he fled from this City of Destruction.

"The thought of these things would kill me if it were not for a dream which I had last night, and for what a guest who came here at dawn has told me. So come, my dear ones, let us make our way at once to the gate that leads to the Celestial City. We will find your father and be there with him and his friends."

Then her first two sons burst into tears of joy because of what Christiana told them.

The Two Friends

Now while they were getting ready to go, two friends of Christiana came up to her house and knocked at the door. To them she said, "If you come in God's name, come in."

This mode of speech from the lips of Christiana struck them as strange. Yet they came in and said, "Pray, what do you mean by this?"

"I mean to leave my home," said she to Mrs. Timorous, for that was the name of one of these friends.

Questions and Answers

Timorous: "Why, pray tell me?"

Christiana: "To go to my dear Christian." And with that she wept.

Timorous: "Nay, can it be so? Who or what has brought you to this state of mind?"

Christiana: "Oh, my friend, if you did but know as much as I do, you would be glad to go with me."

Timorous: "What new idea have you got hold of that draws your mind away from your friends and tempts you to go no one knows where?"

Christiana: "I dreamed last night that I saw Christian. Oh, that my soul were with him now! The Prince of the place has sent for me. One came to me at sunrise and brought me this note to tell me to go there. Do read it, I pray you."

 Foolish Advice

Timorous: "Ah, how mad to run such risks! You have heard, I am sure, from our friend Obstinate, what Christian met with on the way. For Obstinate and Pliable went with him until they, like wise men, came back through fear. You heard how he met with the lions and Apollyon. You know what he saw in the Valley of the Shadow of Death. You have heard other things that make my hair stand on end to hear of. Think, too, of these four sweet boys who are your own flesh and bone. Though you should be so rash as to wish to go, yet for their sake, I pray you keep at home."

Christiana's Answer

But Christiana said, "Tempt me not, my neighbor. These toils and snares that you tell me of shall not keep me back. They only serve to show me that I am in the right. Troubles must first be felt, then joy. So since you came not to my house in God's name, as I said, I pray you to be gone, and tempt me no more."

Then Timorous said to Mercy, "Let us leave her to her own ways, since she scorns all that I say."

Mercy's Wise Choice

But Mercy thought that if her friend Christiana must leave, she would go part of the way with her to help her. She took some thought, too, of her own soul. What Christiana had said had touched her, and she felt she must have some talk with this friend. If she found that truth and life were in Christiana's words, she would join her with all her heart.

So Mercy said to Timorous, "I came with you to see Christiana. Since she is leaving town on this day, I think the least I can do would be to walk a short way with her to help her on her way." But the rest she kept from Timorous.

Timorous: "Well, I see you have a mind to play the fool, too. Listen to me while there is time, and be wise."

So Mrs. Timorous went to her own house, and Christiana, with her four boys and Mercy, went on her way.

"Mercy," said Christiana, "I am glad that you want to start me on my way."

Then said young Mercy (for she was quite young), "If I thought it would be good to go all the way with you, I would not go back at all to the town."

Christiana's Offer

Christiana: "Well, Mercy, cast your lot in with mine. I know where our journey will lead us. Christian is where he would not fail to be for all the gold in the mines of Spain. You shall not be sent back, for the King Who has sent for me and my boys is One Who will not turn away from those who seek Him. If you like, I will hire you. You shall go as my maid and yet shall share all things with me. But please, do go."

Mercy: "But how do I know that I shall be let in? If I thought I should have help from Him from Whom all help comes, I would go at once, no matter how rough the way may be."

Christiana: "Well, Mercy, I will tell you what I would have you do. Go with me as far as to the Wicket Gate, and there I will ask. If the keeper of the gate gives you no hope, you can go back to your home."

Mercy: "Well, I will go with you, and the Lord grant that I may dwell in the land for which my heart yearns."

Christiana then felt glad that she had a friend to join her and that that friend should have so great a concern for her soul.

Mercy's Great Regret

So they went on their way; but Mercy looked so sad that Christiana said to her, "What ails you? Why do you weep?"

Mercy: "Oh, who could but weep to think of all the dear friends that we have left behind in our wicked city?"

Christiana: "You feel for your friends as my good Christian did for me when he left me. It saddened him to learn that I did not believe as

he did. And now you, I, and these dear boys follow his path because of his prayers. I hope, Mercy, that these tears of yours will not be shed in vain, for He Who could not lie has said that they who sow in tears shall reap in joy."

Thinking It Through

1. What changed Christiana's mind about what her husband had done?

2. Why did Mrs. Timorous not want Christiana to leave?

3. How far did Mercy plan to go with Christiana?

2 Timothy 2:22

"Flee also youthful lusts: but follow righteousness, faith, charity, peace, with them that call on the Lord out of a pure heart."

Chapter 22

ow when Christiana came up to the Slough of Despond, she and her sons stopped short. Christiana told them that this was the place into which her dear Christian had fallen. But Mercy said, "Come, let us try; all we have to do is to keep the steps well in view." Christiana slipped once or twice in the mud, but at last they got through the slough. Then they heard a voice say to them: "Blessed is she who hath faith, for those things which were told her of the Lord shall come to pass."

So they went on once more, and Mercy said, "Were I as able as you to get in at the gate, I think no Slough of Despond could keep me back."

"Well," said Christiana, "you know your state, and I know mine. It will be a hard journey for both of us because of the many dangers that we must face as we travel toward that land."

---

allow—to permit
faint—to lose consciousness
firm—steadfast; solid; hard

bold—daring; forward
myrrh—a yellowish-brown resin used as an ointment

 ## The Gate

When they came to the gate, they thought for some time about what they should say to Him Who stood there. Since Mercy was not as old as her friend, she said that Christiana must speak for all of them. So she gave a knock, and then (like Christian) two more; but no one came.

Now they heard the fierce bark of a dog, which made them shake with fear. For a while, they did not dare to knock a third time, lest the dog should attack them. So they knew not what to do: they dared not knock, for fear of the dog. They dared not to go back, lest He Who kept the gate should see them as they went and might not like it. At last they gave a knock four times as loud as the first.

The Keeper of the Gate

Then He Who stood at the gate said, "Who is there?" The dog barked no more, and the gate opened wide for them to come in.

Christiana fell to her knees and said, "Let not our Lord be angry that we have made this loud noise at His gate."

At this He said, "Where do you come from, and what is it that you would have?"

Christiana said, "We come from the same town that Christian came from. We beg to be let in at this gate that we may go on our way to the Celestial City. I was the wife of Christian, who now is in the land of joy."

With that, He Who kept the gate threw up His arms and said, "What! Is she now become a pilgrim, who, but a short time ago, hated that life?"

The Pilgrims Enter

Then Christiana bent her head and said, "Yes, and these are my dear sons." So He took her in; and when her four sons had gone through, He shut the gate. When this was done, He said to a man close by, "Sound the horn for joy!"

But now that Christiana was safe through the gate with her boys, she thought it time to speak a word for Mercy. So she said, "My Lord, I have a friend who stands at the gate, who has come here for the same reason that I did. Her heart is sad because she thinks that she comes without invitation, for she received no word from Christian's King, as I did."

 ## Loud Knocking

Outside, Mercy became more frightened as she waited. Her fear of not being allowed to enter the gate became so great that she began banging on the door. Christiana, who was still explaining Mercy's plight to the Gate-Keeper, was startled by the loud knocking.

Then said He, "Who is there?"

Christiana answered, "It is my friend."

So He opened the gate to look out, but Mercy had fainted from the fear that she should not be let in.

Then He took her by the hand and said, "Fear not; stand firm on thy feet. Tell Me from where thou art come and for what purpose."

Mercy: "I do not come as my friend Christiana does, for I was not sent for by the King, and I fear I am too bold. Yet if there is grace to share, I pray Thee let me share it."

Mercy Enters In

Then He took her once more by the hand, led her in, and said, "All may come in who put their trust in Me, no matter what brought them here."

Then He told those that stood by to bring her some myrrh, and in a while she felt better.

Thinking It Through

1. How did the Gate-Keeper feel about Christiana's arrival? How does Jesus feel when anyone asks Him into his heart? Why?

2. Why was Mercy afraid that she would not be let in at the gate? Did she need to be afraid?

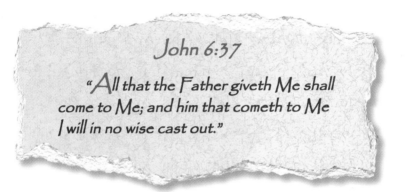

John 6:37

"All that the Father giveth Me shall come to Me; and him that cometh to Me I will in no wise cast out."

Chapter 23

 ow I saw in my dream that He spoke good words to Mercy, Christiana, and her boys, to gladden their hearts. And He took them up to the top of the gate, where He left them for a while. Christiana said, "Oh my dear friend, how glad I am that we have all gotten in!"

Mercy: "You may be happy, but I most of all have cause for joy."

Christiana: "When I stood at the gate and none came to me, I thought that all our pains had been for nothing."

 ## Mercy's Fears

Mercy: "But my worst fears came when I saw Him Who kept the gate grant you your wish and yet take no heed of me. This made me think of the two who ground at the same mill, and that I was the one who was left. I found it hard not to cry out, 'I am lost! I am lost!'"

---

grant—to give
rude—discourteous; offensive

142

Christiana: "I thought you were going to force your way in."

Mercy: "Ah, me! You saw that the door was shut to me and that a fierce dog was not far off. Who, with so faint a heart as mine, would not give loud knocks with all her might? But pray, what said my Lord at this rude noise? Was He not angry with me?"

Christiana: "When He heard your loud thumps at the door, He smiled. To my mind, what you did seemed to please Him well. But it is hard to guess why He keeps that dog. Had I known of it, I fear that I would not have had the courage to come. But now that we are safely in, I am glad with all my heart."

One of Christiana's boys said, "Pray, ask to have a chain put on the dog, for it will bite us when we go near it."

Praise unto the Lord

Then He Who kept the gate came down to them once more, and Mercy fell with her face to the ground and said, "Oh, let me bless and praise the Lord with my lips."

So He said to her, "Peace be to thee; stand up."

The Fierce Dog

But she would not rise until she had heard from Him why He kept so fierce a dog in the yard. "I do not own the dog," He replied. "It belongs to one who lives nearby. In truth, it serves no purpose but to cause those who come here to turn back from My gate by the sound of its voice. But if thou had known more of Me, thou would not have feared the dog. The poor man who goes from door to door begging will run the risk of being bitten by a dog. Shall a dog keep thee from Me?"

Mercy: "I spoke of what I knew not; but, Lord, I know that Thou doest all things well."

Then Christiana rose to go on her way. So He led them and set them in the right path, as He had done to Christian. And as they went, Christiana sang a hymn: "We turn our tears to joy and our fears to faith."

Thinking It Through

1. How did the pilgrims feel when they entered into the gate? How does a person always feel when he asks Christ to come into his heart?

2. Did the Gate-Keeper seem pleased when Mercy kept knocking? Why?

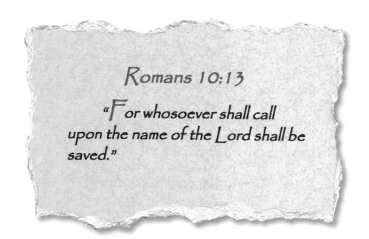

Romans 10:13

"For whosoever shall call upon the name of the Lord shall be saved."

Chapter 24

They had not gone far when they saw some fruit trees, the boughs of which hung over the top of a wall that was built around the grounds of the fierce dog's owner. At times those who came that way would eat the fruit at their own risk. Since the fruit was ripe, Christiana's boys knocked some down and ate some of it. Christiana rebuked the boys and said, "That fruit is not ours." But she knew not then whose it was. Still, the boys continued to eat the fruit.

---

bough—a large branch
rebuke—to criticize sharply
reliever—one who helps or relieves

Now when they had
gone a short distance
from the place, they
saw two men, who
with bold looks
came running
down the hill to
meet them. With
that, Christiana
and her friend
Mercy drew down
their veils. The

boys went ahead of them to keep them on the
path. Then the men came up to them, but Christiana
said, "Stand back, or go by in peace, as you should."
Yet they took no more heed of her words than if they
had been deaf.

Christiana, who did not like their looks, said, "We
are in a hurry and can not stay. Our purpose is a
matter of life and death." With that, she and the rest
made an attempt to pass, but the men would not let
them. So with one voice they all set up a loud cry.

Now, as they were not far from the field gate, they were heard from that place. Some of those in the lodge came out in haste to catch these bad men. When the men saw them coming, however, they leaped over the wall to the ground where the dog was kept.

Reliever: "When you were at the gate, why did you not ask Him who stood there to take you on your way and guard you from harm?"

Christiana: "Ah, sir, the joy we felt when we were let in drove from our thoughts all fears to come. And how could we think that such bad men could lurk in such a place as this? True, it would have been well for us if we had thought to ask Him. But since our Lord knew it would be for our good, why did He not send someone with us?"

Reliever: "You did not ask. When we need something, it pleases Him that we should ask for it."

Christiana: "Shall we go back to my Lord, tell Him we wish we had been more wise, and ask for a guard?"

Reliever: "You do not need to go back, for wherever you go, you will have need of nothing. Just don't forget to ask for what you need."

When he had said this, he left; and the rest went on their way.

Thinking It Through

1. Why did Christiana scold her sons?

2. Why did the boys think it was safe to steal the fruit? Do you ever do wrong things because you think no one will see you?

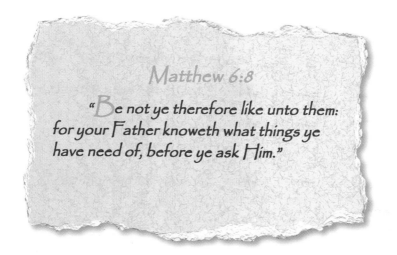

Matthew 6:8

"Be not ye therefore like unto them: for your Father knoweth what things ye have need of, before ye ask Him."

Chapter 25

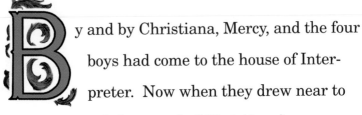

By and by Christiana, Mercy, and the four boys had come to the house of Interpreter. Now when they drew near to the door, they heard the sound of Christiana's name. The news of her flight had caused great excitement, but those inside knew not that she stood at the door. At last she gave a knock, as she had done at the gate. There came to the door a young maid, Innocent by name.

Christiana: "We heard that this is a place of rest for those that go by the way. We pray that we may be let in, for evening is come, and we do not want to go on at night."

Excitement and Joy

Innocent then ran in, and said to those inside, "Can you guess who is at the door? It is Christiana, her boys, and her friend!"

---

innocent—pure; not guilty
refuse—to resist doing something
trough (trôf)—a long, low bin for food or water

brood—a family of young
shield—to guard, to protect
spy—to look; to see

So they leaped for joy, and went to tell it to their lord. He came to the door and said, "Art thou that Christiana whom Christian left in the City of Destruction, when he set out for the Celestial City?"

Christiana: "I am she, but my heart was so hard that I did not listen to him and refused to go with him. These are his four sons. But now I, too, am come, for I feel sure that no way is right but this."

Interpreter's Welcome

Interpreter: "But why do you stand at the door? Come in! It was but just now that we spoke of you, for we heard that you were on your way. Come, my dear boys, come in; come, my sweet maid, come in." So he took them into the house and bade them sit down and rest.

Everyone in the house wore a smile of joy to think that Christiana was on her way to the Celestial City. They were glad to see the young ones walk in God's ways, and they gave them a kind clasp of the hand to show their good will. They also said kind words to Mercy and told them all to feel at home.

Before supper, Interpreter took them to see all those things that had been shown to Christian. Then they were led to a room in which stood a man with a rake in his hand, who could look no other direction but down toward the ground. There stood one beside him with a crown in his hand, who wanted to trade the crown for the rake. The first man did not even look up, but continued raking up the straws, dust, and sticks which lay on the floor.

The Riches of This World

Then said Christiana, "I think I know what this means. It is a picture of a man of this world, is it not, good sir?"

Interpreter: "Thou art right. His rake shows that his mind is on this world, and that he thinks life in the next world is only a dream. Take note that he does not so much as look up. Most think that straws, sticks, and dust are the great things to live for."

At that Christiana and Mercy wept and said, "Ah, yes, it is too true!"

The Hen and Her Chicks

Interpreter then took them to a room where there were a hen and her chicks. "Watch them for awhile," he said. Soon one of the chicks went to the trough to drink. Each time she drank, she would lift up her head and her eyes to the sky.

"See," said he, "what this bird does, and learn of her from where all good comes. Learn to give to the Lord Who dwells on high the praise and thanks for it. Look once more, and see all the ways that the hen has with her young brood. There is her call that goes on all day long, and there is her call that comes but now and then. She has a third call to shield them with her wings; and her fourth is a loud cry, which she gives when she spies a foe.

"Now," said he, "compare the mother hen with your Heavenly Father, and compare the chicks with those who do His will. The call given all day long is the constant walk with His saints. The call that cometh now and then shows that He hath something good to give us. He hath a call to bring under His wings all those that seek protection. The fourth call is to warn us about those who would harm our souls."

Thinking It Through

1. What is the most important thing to the man with the rake? What do some people consider more important than living for God?

2. Why do you think Interpreter shows the pilgrims these things? Where can we get wisdom for everyday living?

Proverbs 1:5, 7

"A wise man will hear, and will increase learning; and a man of understanding shall attain unto wise counsels."

"The fear of the Lord is the beginning of knowledge: but fools despise wisdom and instruction."

Chapter 26

ow when Christiana, Mercy, and the boys had all had a good night's rest, they rose with the sun and started to leave. But Interpreter told them to wait awhile. "For," he said, "you must leave properly, for such is the rule of the house."

Proper Preparations

Then he told Innocent to take them to the bath, and there to wash the dust from them. This done, they came forth fresh and strong, and Interpreter said, "You look as bright as the moon."

Next he told his servants to bring the seal. When it was brought, he set his mark on them that they might be known in each place where they went.

Then Interpreter said, "Bring garments for them." And their clothing was as white as snow, so

---

properly—in a suitable manner
garments—clothes
pant—to breathe quickly; gasp

gasp—to catch the breath; to breathe heavily
flask—a small bottle
fetch—to get and bring something

that it startled each of them to see the others shine with so bright a light.

 Great-heart

Interpreter then sent for one of his men whose name was Great-heart. He told Great-heart to take them to the House Beautiful, where they would rest.

Then Interpreter, with a good wish for each, left them. So they went on their way, and they sang this:

"O move me, Lord, to watch and pray,
From sin my heart to clear;
To take my cross up day by day,
And serve the Lord with fear."

 The Tomb and the Hill

They next came to the place where Christian's load had been lost in the tomb. Here they paused and gave thanks to Him Who laid down His life to save theirs. Now they went up the hill, which was so steep that the toil made Christiana pant for breath.

"It is easy to see," said she, "that they who love rest more than their souls would choose an easier way to go than this."

Then Mercy said, "Come what may, I must rest for a while."

And James, who was the smallest of the boys, started crying.

"Come, come!" said Great-heart. "Don't stop here. There is a seat ahead of us put there by the Prince." With this, he took the young child by the hand and led him to it. They were all glad to sit down and to be out of the heat of the sun's rays.

Rest

Then said Mercy, "How sweet is rest to them that work! And how good is the Prince to place this seat here that such as we may rest! Of this spot I have heard much, but let us take heed that we sleep not, for that caused poor Christian much trouble."

Then Mr. Great-heart said, "Well, my brave boys, how do you do? What do you think of this hill?"

"Sir," said James, "this hill makes me gasp for breath! I see now that what I have been told is true— that the way to the land of joy is a steep climb. Still, sir, it is worse to go downhill to death than uphill to life."

"You are a good boy," said Great-heart.

Christiana: "Come, will you not drink out of this flask, and eat some fruit, while we sit here to rest? For Mr. Interpreter put these in my hand as I came out of his door."

Now when they had sat there awhile, their guide said to them, "The day grows late. Let us now go on our way."

So they all set out, the boys first, and then the rest. But they had not gone far when Christiana found she had left the flask, so she sent James back to fetch it.

The Lost Scroll

Mercy: "I think this is the place where Christian lost his scroll. How did this happen, sir?"

Great-heart: "We may trace it to two things. One is sleep, and the other is that you cease to think of that which you cease to want. When you lose sight of

a reward, you lose
sight of Him Who
grants it, and the
joy of it will end
in tears."

Thinking It Through

1. While the pilgrims were climbing the hill, what did Christiana say about those who loved rest more than their souls?

2. Rest is sweet only to whom?

Deuteronomy 5:33

"Ye shall walk in all the ways which the Lord your God hath commanded you, that ye may live, and that it may be well with you, and that ye may prolong your days in the land which ye shall possess."

Chapter 27

By and by they came to a small mound with a post on it, where these words were written: "Let him who sees this post take heed of his heart and his tongue that they be not false." Then they went on until they came to two large lions.

Now Great-heart was a strong man, so he had no fear. But the fierce looks of the lions made the boys start, and they all clung to Great-heart.

"How now, my boys! At first, when there was no cause for fear, you marched on as brave as can be. But when a test of your strength came, you shrank."

 ## Giant Grim

Now, when Great-heart drew his sword to force their way through, there came up one Giant Grim, who said in a gruff voice, "What right have you to come here?"

---

mound—a small hill
shrank—grew smaller; retreated
grim—stern or forbidding

slay—to kill
slain—killed
mere—nothing more than

Great-heart: "These folk are on their way to the Celestial City. This is the way that they shall go, in spite of thee and the lions."

Grim: "This is not their way, nor shall they go on it. I am come forth to stop them, and for that purpose I will help the wild beasts."

To say truth, so fierce were these lions, and so grim the looks of him who had charge of them, that the road was grown with weeds and grass because so few people used it. And still Grim bade them turn; for he said, "You shall not pass!"

But their guide came up and struck at him so hard with his sword that he forced him to fall back.

Giant Grim: "Will you slay me on my own ground?"

Great-heart: "It is the King's highway on which we stand, and it is in His way that you have put these beasts. But these who are in my charge, although they are weak, shall travel on in spite of all." And with that Great-heart dealt him a blow that brought him to the ground. So Giant Grim was slain.

Then Great-heart said, "Come now with me, and you shall not be harmed by the two beasts." So they went by, but they were shaking from head to foot at the mere sight of the beasts' teeth and claws.

Thinking It Through

1. Were the pilgrims warned about coming dangers? How are we warned about whom to avoid?

2. Why did Great-heart know that he would defeat Giant Grim?

Jeremiah 20:11

" The Lord is with me as a mighty terrible one: therefore my persecutors shall stumble, and they shall not prevail. . . ."

Chapter 28

At length they came in sight of the lodge. When they reached the gate, the guide gave a knock, and the man at the lodge said in a loud voice, "Who is there?"

Great-heart: "It is I."

Mr. Watchful: "How are you, Mr. Great-heart? What has brought you here at so late an hour?"

Then Great-heart told him that he had come with some friends who were on their way to Zion.

---

dawn—to begin to grow light as the sun rises
psalm—a sacred song or poem used in worship
lute—a stringed musical instrument
chat—to talk

Great-heart Turns Back

Mr. Watchful: "Will you come in and stay until the day dawns?"

Great-heart: "No, I will go back to my Lord tonight."

Christiana: "Ah, sir, I know not how we can part with you, for it is to your brave heart that we owe our lives. You have fought for us, and you have taught us what is right. Your faith and your love have known no bounds."

Mercy: "O that we could have you for our guide all the rest of the way! For how can such weak folk as we are hold out in a path full of toils and snares if we have no friend to take us?"

James: "Pray, sir, stay with us and help us, because the right road is so hard to find."

Great-heart: "As my Lord wills, so must I do. If He sends me to join you once more, I shall be glad to serve you. However, it is your mistake that causes my return. If you had asked my Lord to let me lead you until the very end of the journey, He would have done so. But now I must go back; and so, good Christiana, Mercy, and my dear boys, fare ye all well."

Watchful

Then Watchful, who kept
the lodge, asked
Christiana where
she had come from
and who her
friends were.

Christiana: "I
come from the City of
Destruction, and I was
the wife of Christian, who has entered into Zion."

Then Watchful rang the bell, and there came to
the door a maid, to whom he said, "Go, make it known
that Christiana, the wife of Christian, and her four
boys are come on their way to the Celestial City."

So she went in and told all this. And, oh, what
shouts of joy were sent forth when the maid told the
people of the house those things! So all came with haste
to Watchful, for Christiana still stood outside the door.

Some of them said to her, "Christiana, come in,
thou wife of that good man. Come in, thou blessed
one; come in, and all that are with thee."

So she went in, and the rest with her. They then

sat down in a large room, where the chief of the house came to see them and to cheer his guests. Then he gave each of them a kiss. But since it was late, and Christiana and the travelers were tired from all that had happened that day, they wanted to go to bed.

Christian's Room

"Nay," said those of the house, "take first some meat. Watchful heard that you were on your way, and we had a lamb slain for you." When the meal had come to an end, and they had sung a psalm, Christiana said, "If we may be so bold as to choose, let us be in that room which was Christian's when he was here."

So they took them there. Before she went to sleep, Christiana said, "I did not think when my poor Christian set off with his burden on his back that I would do the same thing one day."

Mercy: "No, nor did you then think that you should rest in the same room as he had done."

Christiana: "And less still that I would ever see his dear face again who was dead and gone, and praise the Lord the King with him. Yet now I think I shall."

Mercy: "Do you hear a noise?"

Christiana: "Hark! as far as I can make out, the sounds we hear come from the lute, the pipe, and the horn."

Mercy: "Sweet sounds in the house, sweet sounds in the air, sweet sounds in the heart, for joy that we are here!"

Thus did Christiana and Mercy chat for awhile, and then they slept.

Thinking It Through

1. Why couldn't Great-heart continue traveling with the pilgrims?

2. Why do you think the lodge-keeper must be watchful?

Isaiah 61:10

"I will greatly rejoice in the Lord, my soul shall be joyful in my God; for He hath clothed me with the garments of salvation, He hath covered me with the robe of righteousness, as a bridegroom decketh himself with ornaments, and as a bride adorneth herself with her jewels."

Chapter 29

t dawn when they woke up, Christiana said to Mercy, "What was it that made you laugh in your sleep last night? Was it a dream?"

Mercy: "Yes, and a sweet dream it was. But are you sure that I laughed?"

Christiana: "Yes, you gave a laugh as if it came from your heart. Pray, tell me about it, Mercy."

Mercy: "I dreamed that I lay in some dark woods weeping and wailing because my heart was so hard. Now I had not been there long when I thought that someone laughed at me and called me a fool. Then I saw a Bright One with wings come up to me. 'Mercy,' he said, 'what ails you?' And when he heard the cause of my grief, he said, 'Peace be to thee.'

"He then came up to wipe off my tears, and had me clad in robes of gold, and put a chain on my neck

---

clad—clothed; covered
admire—to have respect or admiration for
brisk—sharp in tone or manner

wed—to marry
blot—a spot or stain

and a crown on my head. Then he took me by the hand and said, 'Mercy, come this way.' So he went up with me until we came to a gate, at which he gave a knock. Then he took me to a throne on which One sat. The place was as bright as the stars; nay, more like the sun. And I thought that I saw Christian there. So I awoke from my dream. But did I laugh?"

Christiana: "Laugh! Yes, and so you might, to see how well off you were! For if you find the first part true, so you will find the last."

Mercy: "Well, I am glad of my dream, for I hope before long to see it come to pass, so as to make me laugh once more."

 ## Christiana Decides to Stay

Christiana: "I think it is now time to rise and find out what we must do."

Mercy: "Pray, if they should ask us to stay, let us by all means do so, for I should much like to get to know these maids better. I think Prudence, Piety, and Charity have a most pleasing manner."

Christiana: "We shall see what they will do."

So they came down.

Then said Prudence and Piety, "If you will stay here, you shall have what the house will yield."

Christiana: "We are grateful for that."

So they were there for some time, much to their good.

 ## Christiana's Sons

Prudence: "Christiana, I admire you, for you have brought your boys up well. With James I have had a long chat. He is a good boy, and has learned much that will bring peace to his mind while he lives on this earth. And in the world to come it will cause him to see the face of Him Who sits on the throne. For my own part, I will teach all of your sons.

"At the same time," she continued, speaking to the children, "you must still give heed to all that Christiana can teach you. But more than all, you must read the Book of God's Word, which sent your dear father on his way to the land of joy."

 ## Mr. Brisk

After Christiana and the rest had been in this place a week, a man named Mr. Brisk came to court

Mercy, hoping to wed her. Now Mercy was fair to look on, and she was willing to work and to care for those around her. She would knit socks for the poor and give them all that they needed.

"She will make me a good housewife," thought Brisk.

They then told her that the young man seemed to have a great sense of the love of God. However, they had fears that it did not reach his soul, which they feared loved the world too much.

"Nay, then," said Mercy, "I will look no more on him, for I will not have a blot on my soul."

Prudence: "If you go on as you have set out, and work so hard for the poor, he will soon cool."

So the next time he came, he found her at her work.

 ## Mr. Brisk Is Discouraged

"What, still at it?" said he.

Mercy: "Yes."

Mr. Brisk: "How much can you earn in a day?"

Mercy: "I work at these things for the good of those for whom I do them, and more than this, to do the will of Him Who was slain on the cross for me."

With that his face fell, and he came no more to see her.

Prudence: "Did I not tell you that Mr. Brisk would soon flee from you? Yea, he may seem to love Mercy, but Mercy and he could not walk the same road of life side by side."

Thinking It Through

1. What was it about Mercy's dream that made her laugh?

2. Why did Mr. Brisk finally give up courting Mercy?

Galatians 6:9,10

"And let us not be weary in well doing: for in due season we shall reap, if we faint not.

"As we have therefore opportunity, let us do good unto all men, especially unto them who are of the household of faith."

Chapter 30

ow Matthew, the son of Christiana, fell sick; so they sent for Mr. Skill to cure him. He asked, "What does he eat?"

Christiana: "Well, there is no food here but what is good."

Mr. Skill: "This boy has in him some strange food, which will kill him if I do not get rid of it."

The Penalty of Sin

Samuel said to Christiana, "What was it that you saw Matthew pick up and eat when we came from the gate which is at the head of this way?"

Christiana: "It was some of the fruit that grows there."

Skill: "I felt sure that it was some bad food. That fruit hurts more than all, for it is the fruit from

---

skill—ability to perform quickly and well
cure—to restore to health
sorrow—sadness; grief; regret
theft—an act of stealing
brow—the edge or upper part of a high place

Beelzebub's grounds. Did no one warn you of it? Some fall down dead when they eat it."

Then Christiana wept and said, "What shall I do for my son? Pray, sir, do your best to cure him, no matter what the cost."

Medicine for the Soul

Then Skill gave strange drugs to him, which he would not take. So Christiana put one of them to the tip of her tongue. "Oh, Matthew," said she, "it is sweet, sweet as honey. If you love me, if you love Mercy, if you love your life, do take it."

So in time he did, and felt sorry for his sin. The pain left him, so that he could walk with a crutch, and he went from room to room to talk with Mercy, Prudence, Piety, and Charity.

Christiana: "Pray, sir, what else are these pills good for?"

Skill: "They are good for all those that go on their way to the Celestial City."

Christiana: "I pray of you to make me up a large box full of them; for if I can get these, I will take none else."

Skill: "I do not doubt that if a man will but use them as he should, he will not die. But, good Christiana, these pills will be of no use if you do not give them as I have done. They must be given in a glass of sorrow for the sins of those who take them." So he gave some to Christiana and the rest of her boys, and to Mercy. He bade Matthew to keep a good look out that he ate no more green plums; then he gave him a kiss, and went his way.

Joseph's Idea

Now, as they had spent some time here, they prepared to go. Then Joseph, who was Christiana's third son, said to her, "You ought to ask Mr. Interpreter to let Mr. Great-heart be our guide for the rest of the journey."

"Good boy!" said Christiana, "I had not thought of it."

So she wrote a note, and Interpreter said to the man who brought it, "Go, tell them that I will send him."

Great-heart Returns

Great-heart soon came, and he said to Christiana and Mercy, "My Lord has sent you some drink and baked corn, and to the boys, figs and raisins."

The travelers then set off, and Prudence and Piety went with them. But first Christiana bid farewell to Watchful, who kept the gate, and put a small coin in his hand. Then she thanked him for all that he had done for her and her dear boys. She then said to him, "Have you seen men go by since we have been here?"

Watchful: "Yes, I have, and there has been a great theft on this highway, but the thieves were caught."

"I am afraid to go on that road," said Mercy.

Matthew: "Fear not; as long as we have Mr. Great-heart with us to guide us, we shall be safe."

Piety's List

I now saw in my dream that they went on until they came to the brow of the hill, when Piety said, "O,

I must go back to fetch that which I meant to give to Christiana and Mercy. It was a list of all those things which they had seen at the house where we live." When she had fetched it, she said, "I beg of you to look on this from time to time, and remember it for your good."

Thinking It Through

1. What made Matthew sick?

2. What really healed Matthew? How can we be healed from the sickness of sin?

2 Timothy 2:21

"If a man therefore purge himself from these, he shall be a vessel unto honor, sanctified, and meet for the master's use, and prepared unto every good work."

Chapter 31

hey now went down the hill to the Valley of Humiliation. It was a steep hill, and their feet slid as they went on. But they took great care, and when they had reached the foot of it, Piety said to Christiana, "This is the valley where Christian met with Apollyon and where they had that fierce fight which I know you must have heard of. But be of good cheer; as long as we have Mr. Great-heart to guide us, there is nothing here that will hurt us, except those sights that spring from our own fears."

Christian's Sign

James: "See, there is a sign with words on it. I will go and read it."

So he went and found that these words were cut on it: "Let the slips which Christian met with while

---

forgetful—having a poor memory; not remembering much
meditate—to think upon or ponder
accidentally—happening by accident
vile—evil; wicked
brute—a beast

he was coming through here, and the fights he had in this place, warn all those who come to the Valley of Humiliation."

Mr. Great-heart: "It is not so hard to go up this hill as it is to go down, and that can be said about few hills in this part of the world. But we will remember Christian; he is at rest, and he had a brave fight with the enemy. Let Him Who dwells on high grant that we fare no worse when our strength is put to the test. This valley brings forth much fruit."

The Rich Poor Shepherd

Now, as they went on, they met a poorly clothed boy who kept watch on some sheep. He had a fine fresh face, and as he sat on a bank he sang a song.

"Hark," said Great-heart, "to the words of that boy's song."

"He that is down needs
fear no fall,
He that is low, no pride;
He that is humble,
ever shall
Have God to be his
guide."

Then said Great-heart, "Do you hear him? I dare say this boy leads as happy a life as he that is clad in silk, and that he wears more of what is called 'heart's ease.'"

Forgetful Green

Samuel: "In what part of this valley was it that Apollyon fought Christian?"

Great-heart: "The fight took place at that part of the plain which is called Forgetful Green. If those who go on their way meet with a shock, it is because they have forgotten good which they have received from the hand of Him Who dwells on high."

Mercy: "I think I feel as well in this place as I have felt anywhere else on our journey. This valley has a sweet grace, and it pleases my mind. I love to be in such a spot as this, where there are no wagon wheels to make a racket. Here one may think about what he is, where he came from, and for what the King has made him. Here one may meditate and pray."

Rough Travel

Just then they thought that the ground below them shook. But the guide told them to be of good cheer, and to watch their step, lest they should accidentally fall.

Then James felt sick, but I think the cause of it was fear. Christiana gave him some of the drink which Mr. Interpreter had put into her hands, and three of the pills which Mr. Skill had given them, and the boy soon got well.

The Beast

They then went on awhile, and Christiana said, "What is that thing on the road? A thing of such a shape I have not seen in all my life!"

Joseph said, "What is it?"

"A vile thing, child; a vile thing!" said she.

Joseph: "But what is it like?"

Christiana: "It is like—I can't tell what. Just then it was far off; now it is near."

Great-heart: "Well, well, let them that are most afraid keep close to me."

Then it went out of sight of all of them.

 ## Great-heart's Courage

But they had not gone far when Mercy cast a look back, and saw, as she thought, a great beast come up behind them with a loud roar.

This noise made them all quake with fright, except for their guide, who fell back and put the rest in front of him. But when the brute saw that Great-heart meant to fight him, he drew back and was seen no more.

Thinking It Through

1. Why do you think Christian left so many signs and warnings?

2. Even though the little shepherd boy was poor, why was he thought of as being rich?

3. What happened to the horrible beast?

Proverbs 14:26, 28:1

"In the fear of the Lord is strong confidence: and His children shall have a place of refuge.

"The wicked flee when no man pursueth: but the righteous are bold as a lion."

Chapter 32

ot long after they left the spot, a great mist fell on them, and they could not see.

"What shall we do?" said they.

Their guide told them not to fear, but to stand still while he tried to find a safe path out.

Then said Christiana to Mercy, "Now I see what my poor, dear Christian went through; I have heard much of this place. Poor man, he went here in the dead of the night, and no one was with him. Who can tell what the Valley of the Shadow of Death should mean, until they actually see it? To be here fills my breast with fear!"

 Prayer

Great-heart: "It seems now as if the earth were a prison around us. I would not boast, but I believe that

---

mist—a damp fog
proceed—to continue; to go on
stout—bulky; solid; strong
inn—a roadside hotel

feast—a large meal; a banquet
Samaritan—a person from Samaria; a person who helps others

we shall still find our way out. Come, let us pray for light to Him that can give it."

So they did weep and pray. And since the path was now smoother, they proceeded much faster.

Mercy: "To be here is not as sweet as it was at the Gate, or at Mr. Interpreter's, or at the house which we just left."

Samuel's Wisdom

"Oh," said one of the boys, "it is not so bad to go through this place as it is to dwell here for all time; for this place surely shows us how blessed the city is to which we go, and how little we have left behind us."

Great-heart: "Well said, Samuel; thou dost now speak like a man."

Samuel: "Why, surely, if I get out of this place, I think I shall prize that which is right and good more than I have done all my life."

Great-heart: "We shall find our way out by and by."

So on they went.

 ## Snares

Joseph: "Can we not see the end of this valley yet?"

Great-heart: "Look to your feet, for you will soon be where the snares are."

So they took great care where they stepped.

Great-heart: "Men come here and bring no guide with them; that is why they die from the snares they meet with in the way. Poor Christian! It is strange he made it out of this place safely. But God dwelt in his soul, and he had a stout heart of his own, or else he could not have done it."

Christiana: "I wish that there were an inn here where we could all rest."

"Well," said Mr. Honest, one whom they had just met, "there is such a place not far off."

 ## A Welcome Rest

So there they went, and the host, whose name was Gaius, said, "Come in, for my house was built for pilgrims such as you."

Great-heart: "Good Gaius, let us eat. What have you for us to eat? We have gone through many dangers and stand much in need of food."

Gaius: "It is too late for us to go out and seek food, but anything we have you may eat."

Honest and Gaius

The meal was then prepared. Near the end of the feast, as they all sat around the table to crack nuts, old Honest said to Gaius, "Tell me what this verse means:

> A man there was, and some did
>   count him mad;
> The more that this man gave,
>   the more he had."

Then all the youths gave a guess as to what Gaius would say about it. He sat still awhile, and then said:

> "He that gives his goods to the poor,
> Shall have as much and ten times more."

Joseph: "I did not think, sir, that you would know its meaning."

Gaius: "Ah! I have learned from my Lord to be kind, and I find I gain by it."

They spent ten days at the house of Gaius, and then they left. But on the last day he made them a feast, of which they all ate and drank.

The Good Samaritan

Great-heart: "Now, Gaius, the hour has come that we must be gone. Tell me what I owe you for this long stay at your inn, for we have been here for quite some time."

Gaius: "At my house no one pays; for the good Samaritan told me that I was to look to him for all my expenses."

Thinking It Through

1. When did the path get smoother? What does this tell us?

2. What is the value in going through the dark and dangerous places?

3. Did the pilgrims have to pay Gaius for staying at his lodge? Why? What do you know about the Good Samaritan?

Psalm 37:4, 5

"Delight thyself also in the Lord; and He shall give thee the desires of thine heart.

"Commit thy way unto the Lord; trust also in Him; and He shall bring it to pass."

Chapter 33

They now left him and went on their way. They met with all kinds of dangers and fears, and finally they came to a place which was called Vanity Fair. There they went to the house of Mr. Mason, who said to his guests, "If there be anything that you need, just say so, and we will do what we can to get it for you."

"Well, then," said they, "we should like to see some of the good folk in this town."

---

rid—to make free of; to remove
fold—a pen for keeping sheep

 Mr. Mason

Mason gave a stamp with his foot, at which his servant Grace jumped up. He sent her to fetch some of his friends who were in the house, and they all sat down to a meal.

Then said Mr. Mason, as he held out his hand to point to Christiana, "My friends, I have guests here who are on their way to Zion. But who do you think this is? This is the wife of Christian, whom, with his friend Faithful, the men of this town did treat so badly."

"Well," said they, "who would have thought we would meet Christiana at this place! May the King Whom you love and serve bring you where He is, in peace!"

Vanity Fair Is Changed

They then told her that the blood of Faithful had lain like a load on their hearts, and that since they had killed him, no more men had been sent to the stake at Vanity Fair. "In those days," they said, "good men could not walk the streets, but now they can show their heads."

Christiana, her sons, and Mercy made this place their home for many years.

 The Snake

Now, one day, a huge snake came out of the woods and killed some of the folk of the town. No one was brave enough to face it, but all fled when they heard that it came near, for it took off the babies by scores.

But Great-heart and the rest of the men who were at Mr. Mason's house made up their minds to kill this snake, and so rid the town of it. So they went forth to meet it, and at first the snake did not seem to notice them. But since they were strong and well-armed men, they drove it back. Then they lay in wait for it and fell on it, until at last they knew it would die of its wounds.

By this deed, Mr. Great-heart and the rest won the
admiration of the whole town.

The Good Shepherd

The time now drew near for them to go on their
way. Mr. Great-heart went first
as their guide, and I saw in my
dream that they came to
the stream on this side
of the Delectable
Mountains. Fine
trees, the leaves
of which were good
for the health, grew on
each bank, and the fields were green all year around.

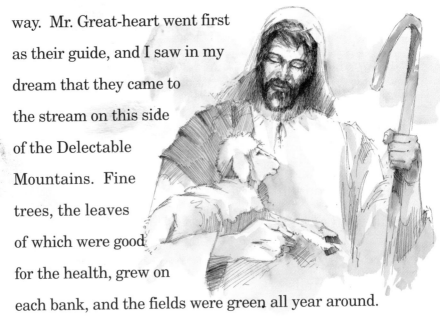

Here they could lie down and be safe. Here, too, there were folds for sheep, and a house was built in which to raise the lambs. There was One Who kept watch over them, Who would take them in His arms and lay them on His breast.

Thinking It Through

1. With whom did the pilgrims stay in Vanity Fair?

2. What changed Vanity Fair?

3. How did Great-heart win the respect of the people of Vanity Fair?

4. Who was the Good Shepherd Who took care of the sheep?

Isaiah 55:11

"So shall My word be that goeth forth out of My mouth: it shall not return unto Me void, but it shall accomplish that which I please, and it shall prosper in the thing whereto I sent it."

Chapter 34

When they went to By-Path meadow, they sat on the stile to which Christian had gone with Hopeful when Giant Despair shut the two up in Doubting Castle. They sat down to think what would be the best thing to do now that there were so many of them and they had such a man as Mr. Great-heart to guide them. They thought it might be well to pull down Doubting Castle and free any poor souls shut up there who were on their way to the Celestial City. One said this thing, and one said that. At last Mr. Great-heart said, "We are told in the Book of God's Word that we are to fight the good fight. And, I pray, with whom should we fight if not with Giant Despair? So who will go with me?"

Christiana's four sons said, "We will," for they were young and strong.

---

despondency—the state of being discouraged or hopeless
mire—deep mud or slush
slothful—lazy

Great-heart Slays Giant Despair

When they knocked at the gate, Giant Despair and his wife came to them.

Giant Despair: "Who or what is he that is so bold as to come to the gate of Giant Despair?"

Great-heart: "It is I, a guide to those who are on their way to Zion. And I charge thee to throw open thy gates and come forth, for I am come to slay thee and pull down thy house."

Giant Despair: "What, shall such as Great-heart make me fear? No!"

So he put a helmet of steel on his head, and with a breastplate of fire, and a club in his hand, he came out to fight his foes.

Then Great-heart and Christiana's four sons came up to him, and they fought for their lives, until Despair was brought to the ground and put to death by Great-heart. Next they attacked his house, but it took six days to pull it down. They found there Mr. Despond-ency and Much-afraid, his child, and set them free.

The Delectable Mountains

Then they all went on to the Delectable Moun-tains. They made friends with the men who kept watch on their flocks, and these men were as kind to them as they had been to Christian and Hopeful.

"You have brought a large group with you," said they. "Pray, where did you find them?"

So their guide told them how it had come to pass.

The Enchanted Ground

By and by they got to the Enchanted Ground, where the air makes men sleep. Now they had not gone far when a thick mist fell on them, so that for awhile they could not see. Since they could not see

where they were going, they kept near their guide by calling to him. But one fell in a bush, while one stuck fast in the mud, and some of the young ones lost their shoes in the mire. "Oh, I am sinking!" said one. "Where are you?" cried the next; while a third said, "I am caught fast in this bush."

Then they came to a bench, Slothful's Friend by name, which had shrubs and plants round it to screen those who sat there from the sun. But Christiana and the rest gave such good heed to what their guide told them that, although they were worn out with toil, there was not one of them that had so much as a wish to stop there. They knew that it would be death to sleep even for a short time on the Enchanted Ground.

Our Map: God's Word

Now as it was still dark, their guide lit a fire that he might look at his map (the book of God's Word); and if he had not done so, they would all have been lost, for just at the end of the road was a pit full of mud, and no one can tell how deep.

Then I thought, "How helpful this map is, to tell us what way we should take; and yet so few use it."

Thinking It Through

1. Why did Great-heart decide to attack Giant Despair?

2. How is God's Word our map?

3. Every time the pilgrims prayed, they were helped. What does this tell us about God?

John 14:13, 14

"And whatsoever ye shall ask in My name, that will I do, that the Father may be glorified in the Son.

"If ye shall ask any thing in My name, I will do it."

Chapter 35

hen they came to the land of Beulah, where the sun shines night and day. Here they rested and ate of the fruit that hung from the trees around them. But the land was so beautiful that they only slept for a short time. The bells rang to such sweet tunes, and such a bright light burst on their eyes, that they soon rose to walk to and fro on this bright way where no sinful feet dare to tread.

And now they heard shouts rise up, for a messenger had come from the Celestial City with words of great joy for Christiana, the wife of Christian. They searched for her, and they found the house where she was staying.

The Joyous Message

Then the messenger put a note in her hands, the words of which were: "Hail, good Christiana! I bring

---

hail—a greeting used in the past, as we use *hello* today
cling—to hold onto tightly

thee word that the Lord calls for thee, and waits for thee to stand near His throne in robes of white, in ten days' time."

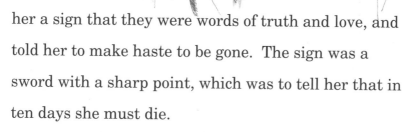

When the messenger had read the note to her, he gave her a sign that they were words of truth and love, and told her to make haste to be gone. The sign was a sword with a sharp point, which was to tell her that in ten days she must die.

Christiana heard with joy that her toils would soon be at an end and that she should once more live with her dear Christian.

Christiana Prepares to Die

She then sent for her sons and their wives to come to her. To them she gave words of good cheer. She told them how glad she was to have them near her at such a time. She sought, too, to make her own death useful to them, from this time up to the hour when each of them would have to leave this world.

Her hope was that it might help to guide them on their path, that the Faith which she had taught them to cling to would have sunk deep in their hearts, and that all their works should spring from love to God. She prayed that they would keep these words in mind and put their whole trust in Him Who had borne their sins on the Cross.

When the day came that she must go forth to the world of love and truth, the road was full of those who wanted to see her start on her way; and the last words that they heard her say were, "I come, Lord, to be with Thee."

Thinking It Through

1. The book says that no sinful feet dare tread in Beulah. Will there be sinners in Heaven? Why?

2. Heaven is full of beautiful, wonderful sights. But will this be the best thing about Heaven? What is the best thing about Heaven?

1 Corinthians 15:54–57

"So when this corruptible shall have put on incorruption, and this mortal shall have put on immortality, then shall be brought to pass the saying that is written, Death is swallowed up in victory.

"O death, where is thy sting? O grave, where is thy victory?

"The sting of death is sin; and the strength of sin is the law.

"But thanks be to God, which giveth us the victory through our Lord Jesus Christ."

The Pilgrim's Dictionary

 ability: the power to do

accidentally: happening by accident

admire: to have respect or admiration for

ail: to give pain or trouble to

aim: purpose; goal; object (noun); to point; to direct

allow: to permit

Apollyon: a name for Satan

armor: a protective body covering made of metal
plates

awe: great wonder, fear, and respect

 bade: asked or told

Beelzebub: a name for Satan

beware: to look out for; to be cautious

Beulah: a place of peace and rest

bid: to command, ask, or tell

bliss: great joy or happiness

blot: a spot or stain

blush: to become red in the face because of shame
or embarrassment

boast: to brag

bold: daring; forward

bough: a large branch

bound: held to

brink: the edge at the top of a steep place

brisk: sharp in tone or manner

brood: a family of young

brow: the edge or upper part of a high place

brute: a beast

burden: a heavy load

 caution: careful forethought to avoid danger

cease: to stop

celestial: relating to Heaven or the heavens

charity: love

chat: to talk

clad: clothed; covered

cleanse: to make clean

cling: to hold onto tightly

cloak: a loose outer garment

conceit: loving or having a high opinion of self

condition: state of mind; state of health

convince: to bring about belief; to prove

creature: a living thing

criticize: to stress the faults of

cure: to restore to health

dawn: to begin to grow light as the sun rises

delectable: delightful; charming

deliverance: a setting free; a rescue or release

despair: loss of hope or confidence

despond: to lose courage or hope

despondency: the state of being discouraged or
hopeless

destroy: to put an end to; to ruin

destruction: the state of being destroyed

difficult: presenting hardships or problems

difficulty: hardship

discretion: the ability to judge what is right or wrong

distress: trouble; a state of danger or desperate
need

doom: condemnation; death; ruin

doth: does

dost: old English form of *do*

dread: great fear

dungeon: a dark underground prison

dwell: to stay or abide

E **ease:** comfort; freedom from pain

enchanted: under a spell; under the influence of
charms

enmity: hatred or ill-will

envy: jealousy

error: a mistake; a departure from the truth

evangelist: a traveling preacher

everlasting: never coming to an end; eternal

faint: to lose consciousness

faith: a firm belief in God; belief in something not seen

feast: a large meal; a banquet

feat: a deed; accomplishment

fetch: to get and bring something

fierce: extremely furious or wild in appearance

firm: steadfast; solid; hard

flask: a small bottle

flee: to run away; to escape from

flight: a running away; fleeing; escaping

flung: threw with force

foe: an enemy

fold: a pen for keeping sheep

forgetful: having a poor memory; not remembering much

formalist: one who pays close attention to forms and ceremonies in religion but misses the true meaning of worship

garments: clothes

gasp: to catch the breath; to breathe heavily

gem: a precious stone; jewel

Gideon: a judge of Israel

Godspeed: a farewell wish for safe travel

good-will: kindness; friendliness

grace: undeserved love or kindness

graceless: not having or experiencing God's grace

grant: to give

grave: serious; solemn; sad

grieved: feeling grief or sorrow

grim: stern or forbidding

gruff: rough; deep; harsh

 hail: a greeting used in the past, as we use *hello* today

harsh: rude; rough; unpleasantly sharp

haste: speed; quickness

heady: willful; headstrong; violent

heed: attention; consideration; notice

hesitate: to hold back; to pause for a moment

hire: to employ; to provide work for

holy: excellent; pure; spiritually perfect

hopeful: having hope; expecting to achieve or receive something in the future

host: the keeper of an inn; a great number

humiliation: the act of damaging a person's dignity or importance

hypocrisy: pretending to be what one is not

 ignorance: the state of lacking knowledge or an education

ignore: to pay no attention to

Immanuel: a name given to Jesus, the Messiah

implacable: not satisfied; incapable of being pleased

inn: a roadside hotel

innocent: pure; not guilty

interpreter: one who explains or tells the meaning of something

in vain: uselessly; for nothing

jeers: mocking or scornful remarks or sounds

jury: a body of men whose job it is to decide the outcome of a trial

legality: the belief that obeying the law will get one to Heaven

lodge: a small house belonging to a servant

lot: one's portion in life

lute: a stringed musical instrument

malice: extreme ill-will; a desire to harm another

mast: a round timber set upright in a ship to support the sails

meadow: a large field or grassland

meditate: to think upon or ponder

mercy: compassion; pity

mere: nothing more than

Midian: People living in this land fought against Israel.

mire: deep mud or slush

misery: a state of suffering and discomfort

mist: a damp fog

mistrust: disbelief

mode: style; method; manner

morality: the holding of moral beliefs and high standards

mound: a small hill

myrrh: a yellowish-brown resin used as an ointment

 nay: no

 obstinate: stubborn

 palace: the house of a king; a large public building

pant: to breathe quickly; gasp

passion: strong desire; outbreak of anger

patience: the ability to bear pain or trials calmly

pause: to stop for a short period of time

pierce: to cut or puncture with a pointed object

piety: reverence toward God

pliable: easy to bend

pout: to cry; to whine; to complain

presumption: blind confidence; passing beyond the ordinary bounds of good behavior

pretend: to make believe; to show falsely

proceed: to continue; to go on

properly: in a suitable manner

prudence: carefulness or caution in making decisions

psalm: a sacred song or poem used in worship

 quake: to shake or shudder

 rage: violent anger; wrath

rank: social position

rascal: a mischievous or dishonest person

rash: hasty; showing lack of caution

realm: area; region

reap: to harvest; to gather

reassurance: restored confidence

rebuke: to criticize sharply

reel: to turn or move round and round; to whirl

refuse: to resist doing something

reliever: one who helps or relieves

reunion: a reuniting, or bringing or coming together again

rid: to make free of; to remove

risk: a chance of meeting danger or peril

rude: discourteous; offensive

 Samaritan: a person from Samaria; a person who helps others

scorn: dislike; contempt; hatred; to reject with anger; to show hatred or contempt

scroll: a roll of paper with writing or pictures on it

scum: a thin layer of waste, impurity, or refuse

seal: a piece of wax used to seal a letter or a scroll; to make sure or secure

seek: to search for or look for

Shamgar: a judge of Israel

shield: to guard; to protect

shrank: grew smaller; retreated

simple: having little sense; foolish

sincere: honest; pure; true

skill: ability to perform quickly and well

slain: killed

slay: to kill

slew: killed

sloth: laziness; slowness

slothful: lazy

slough: a place full of soft, deep mud

sluggard: a slow, lazy person

snare: a trap

sole: the only one

soothe: to make calm; to ease

sorrow: sadness; grief; regret

spare: extra

spy: to look; to see

stile: a set of steps used for passing over a fence

stocks: a wooden frame with holes cut for ankles; used for punishment

stout: bulky; solid; strong

strait: small; narrow

strife: a fight; a struggle

strive: to struggle with much effort and energy

superstition: belief based on ignorance or fear

 taunts: insulting words; sarcastic remarks

tempt: to entice to do wrong

theft: an act of stealing

threat: a promise to cause damage or injury

timorous: timid; meek; afraid

tithes: a tenth of one's money given to the Lord as an offering

toil: labor; hard work

tomb: a cave used as a grave

trial: a testing to determine guilt

trough: a long, low bin for food or water

urge: to plead with

V

vain: unsuccessful; useless; empty; conceited

vain-confidence: a confidence having no firm foundation

vain-glory: excessive vanity or conceit; boastfulness

vanity: anything that is worthless

vile: evil; wicked

vow: a solemn promise

W

wages: salary; payment

wail: a long, pitiful cry of grief or pain

watchful: careful; alert; attentive

wed: to marry

weep: to cry

wicket gate: a small gate set near a larger one

woe: a condition of deep suffering or grief

worldly: loving only the pleasures of this world

worthless: having no worth or value

worthwhile: being worth the time or effort spent

wrath: great anger

Y

yearn: to long for

yield: to give up

yonder: at a distance, but within sight

Z

Zion: a name often used for Heaven